Liz Copas was born in Stogursey, near Bridgwater, and spent most of her childhood near the North Downs in Surrey, where she developed her love of botany. After graduating at Reading University with an Honours degree in Horticulture and Crop Protection, she returned to Somerset and has worked for the last twenty years as a Cider Pomologist at Long Ashton Research Station near Bristol. She is now the National Association of Cider Makers' Orcharding Advisor and Field Trial Officer for all the cider growing counties. Liz and her artist husband Ronnie have two sons, one a horticulturist and the other a jazz pianist.

A SOMERSET POMONA

The Cider Apples of Somerset

LIZ COPAS

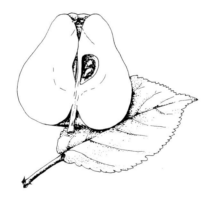

THE DOVECOTE PRESS

IN PRAISE OF CIDER

Cider of the finest quality, is a rich white wine, only second to the best juice of the grape. Cider of this quality can only be made in special seasons from special fruit; just as the finest wines, called 'vintage' wines, can only be produced in rare seasons. Cider making is not so old an industry as grape wine making, because to make a wine you have only to jump into a basket of ripe grapes and dance about till the juice runs out, keep the must or juice for a week to ferment, and then you can get as drunk as Noah in no time. Apples require machinery to crush them and press the juice out, and altogether demand more mechanical and modern lines of thought and treatment than grapes. But that a good pleasant drink can be made from apples is unquestionable.

Proceedings of the Mid-Somerset Agricultural Society's first Cider Conference, Shepton Mallet, 1903

First published in 2001 by The Dovecote Press Ltd
Stanbridge, Wimborne, Dorset BH21 4JD

ISBN 1 874336 87 3

© Liz Copas 2001

Liz Copas has asserted her rights under the Copyright, Designs and Patent Act 1988 to be identified as author of this work

Designed by The Dovecote Press

Typeset in Monotype Sabon

Printed and bound in Singapore

A CIP catalogue record for this book is available from the British Library

1 3 5 7 9 8 6 4 2

CONTENTS

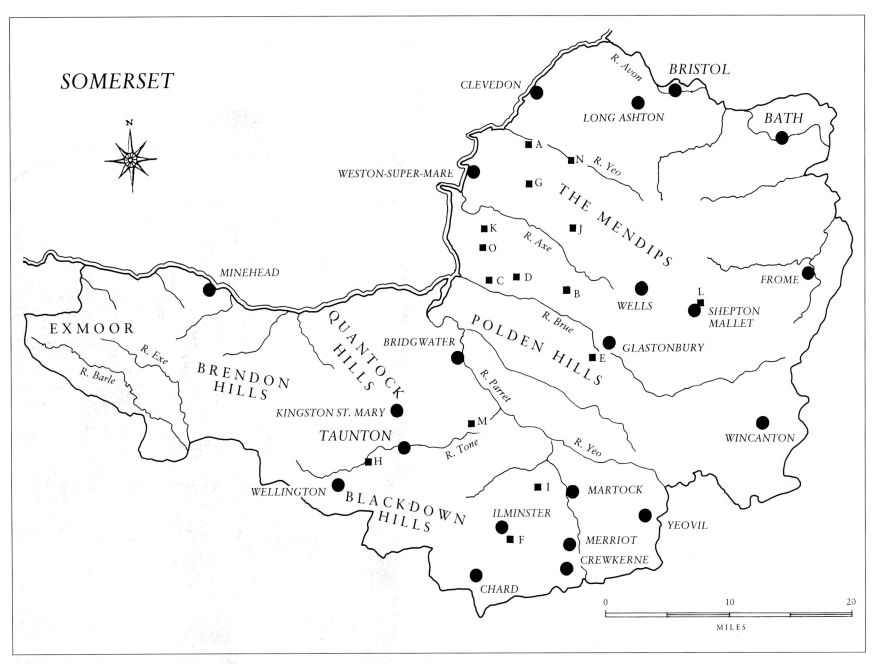

SOMERSET

BRISTOL

CLEVEDON

LONG ASHTON

BATH

A

N R. Yeo

WESTON-SUPER-MARE

G

THE MENDIPS

K

R. Axe

J

O

FROME

C D

B

MINEHEAD

WELLS

L

SHEPTON
MALLET

EXMOOR

R. Exe

QUANTOCK
HILLS

R. Brue

POLDEN HILLS

GLASTONBURY

R. Barle

BRENDON
HILLS

BRIDGWATER

E

R. Parret

KINGSTON ST. MARY

M

WINCANTON

TAUNTON

R. Tone

R. Yeo

H

WELLINGTON BLACKDOWN
HILLS

I

MARTOCK

ILMINSTER

YEOVIL

F

MERRIOT

CREWKERNE

CHARD

0   10   20

MILES

Key to cider makers mentioned in the text.
A Ben Crossman (Hewish); B Wilkins (Wedmore); C Rich's Farmhouse Cider
(Watchfield); D Coombes Cider (Mark); E Hecks (Street); F Perry's Cider Mills
(Dowlish Wake); G Thatchers Cider Company (Sandford); H Sheppey's Cider

(Bradford-on-Tone); I Somerset Cider Brandy Company & Burrow Hill Cider
(Kingsbury Episcopi); J Ashwood Cider (Cheddar); K Dobunni Fruit Farm
(Lympsham): L Matthew Clark PLC (Shepton Mallet); M Parsons Choice (West
Lyng); N Richards (Congresbury); O West Croft Cider (Brent Knoll).

PART I

THE VINTAGE YEARS

Go deep into Somerset, along the winding lanes, and catch glimpses of old orchards through the hedges. Little parcels of trees are squeezed in between the cottages in the village streets. Go out along the levels, where every farmstead with its kitchen orchard close by is on a little island of rising ground, safe from winter water. Even when flashing through by train or on the motorway, there are orchards to be seen. A Somerset orchard is a special thing, be it on a warm spring day when the bees are at the blossom, or in leafy high summer when the sheep browse serenely, or later when the green apples have reappeared from the shelter of the foliage and are colouring up ready for the autumn harvest. Even in winter, there is a special feeling of quiet rest and recuperation before the next season's efforts begin again. Traditional Somerset orchards are an institution, something that has always been there and always will be, reassuringly part of the expected image. To the rest of the world, this is what Somerset is; orchards, apples and cider.

But, is everything as it should be? Where are the cider presses that every farm once had and used? Why do many orchards look so sadly neglected? Why have they not had more care in their old age? And why are so many of them old, where are the young trees planted for the future?

Let's go back over a century to when Queen Victoria reigned. There were orchards then, some exactly where they are now, but many more then filled the fields in-between. Some grew apple varieties still well-known today, but many were lined with trees whose apples bore names that are now unfamiliar. Such orchards had been there a long time. They are part of the structure, a man-made but naturalised element of the environment.

Somerset was always a pastoral county, its land low-lying in many areas and its soils heavy. Cloud laden winds coming in from the Bristol Channel give it a soft, wet climate, well-suited to growing grass. It is perfect country for dairy cattle, and their produce is arguably superior due to the lush feed. Somerset is the home of milk, butter and cheese – a traditional partner of cider.

The cider press was once an essential piece of farm equipment. The chopped apples are layered with straw or cloth in 'cheeses'. Juices flow for several days as the press screw is tightened.

A well kept traditional orchard was, and still is, a dual system. The farm orchard, on its piece of dry land close to the house, gives year round sheltered grazing. The grass starts to grow there first in spring to give an 'early bite' for stock kept in over winter, and the trees enclosed by tall hedges shelter the newly arrived calves and lambs. The stock in turn, do their bit for the orchard by keeping the grass under control and by returning some nutrients to feed the trees.

In Queen Victoria's time, apples, orchards and cider were an integral part of farming life. The orchards would always have a selection of eating and kitchen varieties, good dual purpose fruit and much loved old favourites like Bramleys, Newton Wonder and Blenheims, but the greater part of the orchards would be a mixture of cider apples. Suitable fruit was used in the kitchen as it matured. Some was stored for use in the winter and New Year, and much, even the cookers and eaters that would not keep, went to cider-making. Generally the cider fruit was allowed to ripen and fall naturally, before being collected up into sacks and leant against the trees until the time for cider-making approached. As with all produce there are years of glut and years of shortage. Cider is the best way to store apples in times of plenty, and a consolation in time of shortage.

Somerset always was a difficult county in which to get around. Its roads are small and winding. In the middle of the nineteenth century, much of the land was still undrained. So with transport difficulties, how did the farmers and smallholders get their produce out to the rest of the country? Some of the fruit harvest was sent to Bristol market as eating apples; varieties like Redskins, eye-catching and shiny, and Morgan Sweet, sold to the miners in Wales who liked our sweet fruit. Some produce left the county via Bridgwater, the canals and rivers being an invaluable means of moving goods, and the advent of rail revolutionised some areas. But much of the produce was marketed locally, the farming community remaining self sufficient in many ways.

Somerset agriculture was never wealthy and farm wages have always been low. In Victorian times, most farm labourers were still being paid in kind with bread and cheese and cider. A typical labourer got 3 to 4 pints a day as part of his wages, 6 to 8 pints during haymaking. Some farmers rated their labourers by the amount they could consume. 'A two gallon a day man was worth the extra drink he drank,' said one farmer. Cider might constitute about a fifth of their 'pay'. Parliament tried to put a stop to all this by the Truck Act in 1887. This prohibited the payment of wages with alcoholic drink. Cider 'truck', the unfair exchange, was made illegal, or at least according to London, but the law found it difficult to reach the deepest parts of Somerset and 'truckle' was still part of the way of life right up until the outbreak of the Second World War.

By the end of the nineteenth century, most cider was just made for use on the farm and little was sold elsewhere, except perhaps at the local pub or cider house. Although there were several cider factories in existence, some old-established, others of relatively recent date, their output was small by modern standards. There can have been few good ciders made and many indifferent products available. In some areas the so-called cider was described as a 'synthetic, carbonated, sweetened and artificially flavoured concoction, entirely devoid of apple juice.' The 'genuine article', was almost unknown and unobtainable. Cider matters were no longer hale and hearty. The popularity of cider and cider-making was at its lowest ebb for centuries, and so was it's reputation.

The view of the Herefordshire 'MP for cider', C.W. Radcliffe Cooke, that, 'Ciders and perries are all alike and only to be distinguished from vinegar by a highly discriminating palate,' summed up the general opinion at the time. The future for farm orchards was bleak and the pattern of farm cider-making would never be the same. The wealthy were more likely to drink wine than cider; but fortunately some of them were concerned for its demise, and several rather influential people stepped in to revive cider's flagging reputation.

Sir Robert Neville Grenville, squire of Butleigh from 1886, played a major part in the resuscitation. Happily, he had the good taste to prefer a well-made cider to wine. He predicted that cider would vanish unless something radical was done. He was quoted as being 'impressed by the lack of knowledge of the underlying principles of cider-making at that time and the crudeness of the methods used on the farms', but was astute enough to recognise the possibilities of transforming the crude farm product of only local interest into a valuable national beverage. He began to collect together many cider apple varieties of repute, both English and French, to create an orchard for his experiments.

At about this time, the Hereford based family business, Bulmer's Cider Company, also realised the need to improve the image and standard of their product. They too, began to collect together apple varieties that had acquired a reputation for making a good quality cider. During the 1890s, Neville Grenville enlisted the help of Frederick J. Lloyd, a London analyst, bacteriologist and consultant on cheese-making, to review the

The original National Fruit and Cider Institute (NFCI) premises built at Long Ashton in 1903 comprised a cider house and laboratory. The cider factory on the left was added in 1912.

situation and work towards improvement. Lloyd spent some time trying to determine the composition, sugar and acidity, of the juice of apples most common in the neighbourhood of Butleigh in the search for the varieties best suited to quality cider-making. His greatest difficulty was the fact that no two farmers called the same apples by the same name!

This co-operation, funded by the Bath and West and Southern Counties Society, as it was known then, and by small grants from the Board of Agriculture, was to last ten years. Much of the early evaluation of local varieties was published in the Society's Annual Reports, and gave details of their juice composition. The lists also provide an invaluable record of the names of many of the old cider apple varieties still alive and productive at the time. Many have not been heard of since, and were most likely not sufficiently valuable to deserve preservation, but quite a number

of names do survive to this day. The efforts made at Butleigh Court towards improving cider quality were sufficiently encouraging to induce the Board to agree to the formation of a permanent institute for research and instruction on cider-making and fruit growing. And so, in 1903, the National Fruit and Cider Institute (NFCI), later to become Long Ashton Research Station (LARS), was born.

The site at Long Ashton was leased from Lady Smyth, the owner of the Ashton Court estate. The first buildings to house the early work were ramshackle affairs, dubbed at the time, 'a cart shed and a fowl or pigeon house, the first acquaintance with which is not altogether pleasing.' Finances were tight, but thanks to a generous loan from the Smyth family, they were converted to a milling shed, cellar and stores, and serious work could begin. In 1904 a cider-maker was installed in the Cider House for the first cider-making season.

At the new Institute, Lloyd was to put some science into cider-making. With his background in microbiology, he instructed the

A satisfying conclusion to the cider-making trials. Leading experts at Long Ashton in the early 1930s tasting the results, with Professor B.T.P. Barker on the left.

Long Ashton's Annual Tasting Day in 1936. Sir Stephen Tallents speaking after the distribution of prizes for the cider competition.

One of the last Long Ashton 'Tasting Days'. Cider samples being passed around for comment and judging.

initial staff in the art of controlling yeast fermentation and, acting as a consultant, he was able to solve many of the problems inherent in current cider-making practices by introducing new levels of hygiene. Later on in 1904, a young graduate from Cambridge, B.T.P. Barker, who was specialising in yeast research, came to the Institute as Assistant Director, becoming Director two years later.

When the NFCI was established, the total area of farm orchards of the West Country was about 70,000 to 80,000 acres. It was impossible to assess the number of varieties being used for cider-making at that date, but it was probably thousands rather than hundreds. Barker appreciated the chaotic state of the raw material, and began the urgent and difficult task of sorting the 'sheep from the goats', so to speak. Lloyd's work at Butleigh had started to classify cider apples according to taste, but had hardly begun to assess their vintage quality. As a starting point to the work, Barker sought the opinions of various experienced cider-makers in districts known to produce ciders of merit. They were invited to tender fruit for juice analysis and small-scale cider-making trials under standardised conditions at the Institute.

Between the years 1903-1910, the juice of some 2,000 apples was analysed, enabling Professor Barker to classify cider fruit into the four broad classes that are still used today; sharp, sweet; bittersweet and bittersharp. In his publication *Cider Apple Production* (see page 76), he made his selected list of varieties grouped according to their taste and coined the name 'vintage' for those with the right juice characters. He named each variety, mentioning its principle centre of production and more importantly, gave not only its juice qualities and its cider-making value, but also summarised all its orchard characteristics, good and bad.

It was clear that the vintage quality of an apple's juice could not be determined by its chemical composition alone, but that only by making and tasting its cider could its true value be appreciated. The first tasting day in 1906 was attended by a small group of members who assessed the single-variety ciders. The event attracted much interest among the members who, from year to year, submitted more and more fruit and the Annual Tasting Day at Long Ashton became an established event. By 1924 it was decided to develop the proceedings into an annual Cider Competition. Farmers were invited to submit fruit to be made into cider at the Institute. The resulting ciders, grouped in their appropriate taste classes, were judged the following spring and the awards were presented at the Tasting Day. These events were 'legendary' and attendance at the Tasting Days increased until, by the 1930s, it exceeded a thousand cider-lovers. In their heyday, the lawns at Long Ashton were covered with a marquee enclosing one of the fully grown trees of the orchard. The spread of bread and cheese to accompany the cider tasting was prodigious. (A record remains of a bill for 3cwt of cheese). These competitions not only provided a happy diversion for the members every May, but were also useful in bringing to light many cider apple varieties that would otherwise have remained undiscovered in unknown orchards. Sadly, much to the regret of the participants, these Tasting Days came to an eventual end just before the war in 1939.

Through the enterprise of those influential people of foresight and some of the more progressive cider-makers of the time, the engineering skills marshalled by the work at Butleigh, the backing of the new scientific research at Long Ashton, and the birth of the National Association of Cider Makers in 1920, a unique opportunity arose for English cider-making to develop into a commercial industry. From that foundation, it consolidated and grew into the multi-million pound, prosperous and still expanding industry that it is today.

CIDER IN SOMERSET

It is often said that, like many other good things, the Romans introduced apples to Britain, but when Caesar brought his army over in 55 BC, they would have found plenty of trees here already. The Crab Apple *Malus sylvestris* is indigenous to Britain and still commonly found in woods and hedgerows over much of Somerset, except on the high ground. Many of the wild trees found now are a sub-species, *Malus sylvestris mitis*, which are the descendants of the widely cultivated ones, and frequently seedlings from discarded apple cores. The wild crab itself is also widespread, especially in old woodland. There is further evidence from the old languages that apples have long been cherished, for in Celtic, the apple is 'abhall', and in Cornish, 'avall'. Glastonbury was called 'Avallon' or 'Ynys Avallac', the 'Isle of Apples', by the Iron Age tribes people who were there to greet the Romans.

Other wild apple species such as *Malus pumila* may also have played a great part in the evolution of our English cider apples.

This apple was once widespread in the forests of Asia Minor, the Caucasus, Persia, Armenia and Kurdistan and occurred throughout most of the countries of Europe. These two species, *M. sylvestris* and *pumila*, are the ancestors of our modern rootstocks, some of which are potential cider apples in their own right, with plenty of tannin in their bittersweet juice. It is certain that wandering traders from France and Spain would have brought apples with them, thus introducing an even broader selection of 'genes' for the evolution of the varieties we know today.

The great horticultural 'improvements' to primitive apples came with the arrival of Christianity in Britain. In its wake, monks founded monasteries in quiet, often quite lush and productive, corners of the country. They were keen gardeners, quite able to refer to the classic texts in Greek and Latin, to find the secrets of selection for the best varieties and how to propagate them through budding and grafting. Surely the monks at

Glastonbury had much to build on. Their orchards, or *pomerium*, grew apples and pears for eating, cooking and for making cider, a drink which was much appreciated by monks, as many old illustrations testify! Their cultural methods were obviously successful and have been copied through the ages, even surviving today.

Up until quite recently, many cider-maker farmers used to feed their cattle with the pomace, the spent crushed fruit after the milling and pressing was done. It was common practice to spread the pomace out over the ground for the stock, and wait to see if any of the uneaten apple pips germinated in the spring. These seedlings, which are known as 'gribbles' in Somerset, were grown on until they fruited. Once there was some idea of how they would perform, they were either kept as 'new varieties' if they had the desired taste and character, or used as the basis of a new tree on which to graft another variety. In the past, this resulted in large numbers of indifferent sorts which prompted one early observer, Celia Fiennes, to report of Somerset in 1685, 'It is very fruitful for orchards but they are not curious in the planting of the best sorte of fruite . . . they are likewise as careless when they make sider, they press all sorts of apples together, else they might have as good sider as in any other parts, even as good as the Herriffordshire.'

A remark which had the whiff of rivalry between cider enthusiasts even then. But the cider-makers of Somerset were equal to the challenge and have caused our cider apples to evolve towards excellence over the centuries. The more discriminating farmer would select apples for their flavour and cider-making properties, depending on the taste fashionable in his locality. Bittersweets became the most popular in Somerset but pure sharps and sweets predominated in the southern part of the county near the Devon border. A different type of sweet apple became the favoured taste in the eastern part from Wincanton to Shepton Mallet, but overall, the taste that has clearly always been the Somerset favourite, is the bittersweet.

The other important criteria for selection were some resistance or tolerance to pests and disease, and their potential productivity in the insecurity of a primitive orchard with only the basic care. In the pre-fungicide days, apple trees had no protection against disease and had to be natural survivors. New varieties needed to be fecund, able to crop under subsistence conditions. In practice, most cider apple varieties crop so well and so heavily that they exhaust themselves and have to take a rest the following year. This alternate cropping pattern, known as biennial bearing, is the bug-bear of the modern bush tree orchards.

Most 'varieties' of cider apple remain fairly local in their distribution, some living and dying quite unknown beyond a farm or village. Graft material of many varieties would have been passed round for neighbours to share, but with a strong competitive spirit, owners would have protected their best as a well kept secret ingredient that made their cider special. The more widespread distribution of noted varieties really began in a big way after the establishment of the NFCI at Long Ashton, and the publication of Barker's list of recommendations. Many trial orchards, containing the best varieties, were planted in the county to test the stability of their performance and demonstrate their virtues to keen farmers looking for new material. The example set by Neville Grenville at Butleigh Court had a great influence, encouraging many cider-makers to try some of the best and the more exotic French varieties that he had imported. Some of these, largely 'reinette' types, are still seen in the area today.

A typical orchard of the early twentieth century exists at Cotmill near Pilton where the Williams family have farmed for many years. The orchard contains many good nineteenth century dessert and culinary varieties such as Golden Pippin, Devon Buckland, Darbin Redstreak, Cornish Gilliflower, Christmas Pearmain and the like. Some of these could have been obtained from Scott's Nursery at Merriot near Crewkerne, a prodigious source of excellent fruit tree material. The Cotmill orchard also contains many well-known cider apples; Honeystring, Red Jersey, Sheep's Nose and Dove, all local varieties. The age old method of producing new varieties is amply illustrated by two excellent trees selected from pomace-grown seedlings by Mr Williams senior, and modestly referred to as Williams No.1 and No. 2. These two trees have never been named or propagated for wider use, but they are both potential cider apple 'winners'. There must be plenty more undiscovered treasures like these in the county.

To make an orchard tree, each main variety, the scion variety, is top-worked by grafting a stick to a stem or framework tree. This skilled operation is carried out in the dormant season by experts with a grafting knife. One such grafter who worked for Showerings, Punch Garland of North Wotton, has become a legend through his skills. He is said to have had a wicked sense of humour, and more than once grafted several different varieties into the head of each tree, just to surprise the owner when they bore fruit.

The traditional Somerset method of producing a standard is to grow a tree of a strong variety until it has about ten good sized

Long Ashton in the 1940s. Fruit from Somerset farms being sorted under the direction of the cider-maker, R. Hathaway.

limbs, then, having cut them back to stumps, graft a single stick of the scion to each. The grafting technique, known as the Somerset saddle graft, is still widely used. A stick is inserted under the bark in the usual way but a flap cut from its side is pulled over the stump and fixed across the top. When all the cut surfaces heal and unite with one another, a strongly anchored union is created. It is still used recognised today as the best method for securing a graft stick high in a tree in windy West Country conditions. Lesser 'foreign' methods fail to bind quickly enough and tend to blow out. The fresh grafts on the framework soon grow to form a new head which begins cropping in a few years.

Nowadays the system has changed to suit commercial practice. A strong variety is grown up for two years only in a nursery, then top-worked with a graft at two metres. The Somerset farmer favours the open centred, multi-leadered tree which this method produces. Hereford growers often favour a tree with a centre leader.

In the past, the stem or framework tree was obtained either by growing-on a 'gribble' that did not come up to cider-making expectations, or by using a strong growing, named variety which had proved itself to be suitable for the job. Many of the commonly used stem-builder varieties are triploids, that is, they have three sets of chromosomes compared with the two of normal diploid varieties. This extra genetic 'umph' makes them naturally more vigorous, faster growing and able to form the necessary frame in a shorter time. Although the science behind their vigour was not understood several different varieties were used in the past in different parts of the county, depending on the local knowledge or nursery.

Court Royal, or Sweet Blenheim, was a favourite in many places, especially around the Chard area. It was later superseded over much of mid Somerset by Morgan Sweet when that variety fell out of favour as a dessert apple. Rice's Jersey or Woodbine was a common triploid frame in the district of Glastonbury, adopted by the nursery on the Tor, but in central Somerset where Charles Porter's nursery had some influence in the early part of the twentieth century, Lambrook Pippin was used extensively. Modern tree raisers nearly always use Bulmer's Norman, budding a scion onto a rootstock such as M25 or MM111. This then grows large enough for top-working in two seasons. The major disadvantage of using the strong framework that triploid vigour provides, reveals itself late in the life of many trees. In old orchards, two headed trees with one side full of the little green scabby fruits of Bulmer's Norman, the other side laden with a choice variety, are a familiar sight. Eventually, as the strength of the choice branch wanes, so the frame takes over altogether.

A full sized standard tree needs considerable anchorage to hold it upright for a long and productive orchard life. Although trees are well-staked in their youth, they rely totally on an extensive and healthy root system to support a canopy of branches that may bear a few hundredweight of apples. Before the vegetatively bed-propagated Malling-Merton (M and MM) dwarfing rootstocks became popular, the biggest and strongest root systems were achieved either by seedling or crab rootstocks, propagated from seed. Unlike most seedlings which vary tremendously from their parents, those from the cider varieties Yarlington Mill and Tremlett's Bitter were found to be most uniform and best suited to nursery tree production. They were used by many nurseries up until the 1950s as a rootstock to be budded first with a stem, then a variety, and are much more tolerant of wet soil conditions than the modern rootstocks.

The traditional orchards were usually sited on good, well drained land close to the farmstead. Lower lying sites were often worked or 'landed' to raise the soil into ridges for planting the trees along. The dips or 'grykes' between, filled with water in the winter and drained off the land to the ditches or 'rhynes' surrounding the orchard. In some places the trees were planted on individual humps to raise them up out of the wet. Most standard trees are planted about 30-35 feet apart giving an

Filling and capping bottles in the 1960s. By the time the cider house closed in the 80s, the reputation of Long Ashton's cider had become almost legendary.

orchard with around 40 trees to the acre. This density gives an optimum compromise between the trees and the grass for animal grazing. Trees are far enough apart to encourage good growth and allow air to circulate, so minimising insect pest spread and disease problems. Plenty of light penetrates to encourage the grass below to grow well. Trees usually crop heavily every other year, the 'on year', in a standard orchard, and crops are often modestly around 6 to 10 tons per acre.

Much experimental work went on at Long Ashton during the 1950s to develop bush orchards that might improve on these crop expectations and help meet the increasing demands of the cider-making industry for true cider fruit. Work concentrated on a few chosen apple varieties that had already performed well, budded onto one of the now mass-produced dwarfing rootstocks, primarily MM106.

Bush orchards really took off in the 1970s when both Taunton Cider Company and H.P. Bulmer's Company in Hereford proposed serious Incentive Planting Schemes. Contracts were offered to prospective growers that would guarantee that the company would buy all their cider apple fruit for some 30 years, the expected life of a bush orchard. In addition they would offer some help in establishing the orchard with advice to first-time growers. In the space of less than five years, some 1000 acres of bush orchards were planted in the new bush system, which pushed the planting density up to 250 or more trees to the acre,

An early spiked wheel harvester which made picking up the apples easier but was tough on the fruit. Morris's Hedgehog Apple Picker, cost £65 in 1963.

A modern small scale, self-propelled harvester makes light of working under difficult conditions. The Pattenden Grouse in the wet at Kingston Seymour.

and the crop expectation to a regular 12 tons per acre every year. Some of those orchards, now past middle age, are surpassing all expectations by producing regular outputs of nearer 20 tons per acre.

Bush orchards present a very different picture from the traditional standard orchards. The open view across is obscured by close rows of trees on a short 'leg', budded onto dwarfing rootstocks, usually MM106, perhaps M26, or if more vigour is required, MM111 or M25. Trees take only one or two years to establish before beginning to fruit and should crop well by year five. They may reach 15 to 20 feet high at maturity and can generously yield two or three times as much as a standard orchard every year. They are planted in rows about 18 to 20 feet apart to allow for machinery access, mowers, sprayers and harvesters, for this intensity of planting needs much more looking after. Sheep and cattle are excluded since they would eat the bush trees, so the grass between the tree rows needs mowing regularly through the summer.

At the end of the year the fruit is harvested by shaking it off the trees and picking it up from the ground with a specially designed apple harvester. At such high planting densities, there is a much greater risk of pest and disease problems so a suitable program of fungicide sprays is essential in the spring and early summer. Unlike eating apples which need to look good, cider apples are less fussy. Skin finish is not important and some blemishes can be

tolerated if they have no direct effect on the crop. Although much more costly to plant and maintain, the bush orchard rewards the grower handsomely within a few years, while the farmer with the standard orchard might have to wait for ten years for his first real crop.

The varieties that are likely to be found in bush orchards planted in the first generation in the 1970s are those that performed well in the Long Ashton trials, chosen by the orcharding managers at the cider companies, led by Ray Williams the Cider Pomologist at Long Ashton at the time. Many Somerset orchards planted for Taunton Cider consisted of Michelin and Dabinett, together with Yarlington Mill, Chisel Jersey, Tremlett's Bitter and Taylor's Seedling, in single rows of each across the site for maximum pollination. To a lesser extent rows of Brown's Apple, Harry Masters' Jersey, Stembridge Clusters and Stembridge Jersey were planted.

This arrangement has since proved unsatisfactory since each variety flowers and matures at different times and every row requires different treatment, creating a management nightmare. The more recent trend in the 1990s has been to plant blocks of single varieties, relying on their self-fertility, or several rows of each variety alternating with several rows of a pollinator variety. A system which is much easier to manage.

Of these varieties, Michelin and Dabinett have proved to be exceptional for bush orchards and now cover well over half of the area. Their popularity is beginning to cause management problems of a different sort. The bulk of their fruit and that of the majority of the other bittersweet varieties matures during October, causing a major logistics headache for the cider mills. In an attempt to spread the harvesting season forward, several early maturing varieties are now widely planted; Ashton Bitter, Major, Ellis Bitter and White Jersey, together with the ever popular Somerset Redstreak and Brown's Apple. Many of the other earlies, like Tremlett's Bitter and Nehou, have gone out of fashion through faults like biennialism or poor fruit-keeping qualities, and are no longer planted in bush orchards.

Kingston Black is an oddity. Although it is a poor performer and difficult to manage, it is a variety that fills a specialist niche. As more and more cider-makers are finding a quality market for single variety ciders, this is the best and obvious first choice. A number of Kingston Black orchards have recently been planted to meet this demand, with the reward of a premium price for the fruit.

The 1990s saw the start of the second big expansion of bush orchard acreage. Thanks to excellent promotion by the industry, UK cider sales have made unprecedented growth since the 1980s, topping 500 million litres a year by the turn of the century. Both the main cider companies, Matthew Clark in Somerset and Bulmers in Hereford, launched major incentive planting schemes, more or less along the same lines as in the 1970s, to supply the growing demand for cider apples, and guarantee a home-grown source. To mark the last five years' new bush orchards, the 'Two Millionth' cider apple tree was planted with ceremony at the 2000 Bath and West Show at Shepton Mallet. Bush cider orchards now cover some 5,000 hectares of the South West and West Midlands and planting of the second generation is nearing completion.

A CIDER RENAISSANCE

With this wave of bush trees sweeping the country, what are the prospects for traditional standard orchards? Marcus Govier of Glastonbury makes traditional cider for his lucky regulars with great care, informing us in the official Somerset Cider Video of the duty to look after the orchards handed down to us from the past, and plant them up again for future generations. Paul Rendell of Glastonbury, a traditional furniture maker by trade, makes real cider for a hobby. He lives in an area with a rich cider-making history and collects his apples from old orchards around and about, sometimes from friends and neighbours, sometimes by asking over the hedge for the fruit he sees fallen and left to rot. It is through people like them who are curious enough to know more about the fruit that they use, and cherish each old cider variety for its individuality, that the legend is preserved and perpetuated.

For many traditional orchards, their future is assured for the time being as an essential source of raw material for the small cider-makers, who are far more numerous in Somerset than any other county. Today most small-scale farmhouse cider is still made by the traditional natural method. The juice expressed from the fruit is stored in casks unbunged until the spontaneous fermentation has come to an end. The casks are then bunged and left undisturbed until the cider is required for consumption. Sometimes the liquor is racked off into another cask to aid clarification, but more often it is allowed to remain standing on the 'lees' in the original casks. A hundred years ago, farmhouse cider-making was a rather haphazard procedure, since much of the science behind fermentation was unknown.

Today, though it may still be hard to make a good cider, the art has not been forgotten, and with the benefit of research, the effort is consistently rewarded by success, providing the basic principles are adhered to. The secret of good farmhouse cider is in the selection of the fruit; the right varieties in the right proportions, picked carefully at the right stage of ripeness and used immediately. Even good farmhouse cider, then as now, does not have universal appeal. Traditionally it was a 'man's' drink with a masculine appeal. Some ciders are quite difficult for those used to bland supermarket beverages to appreciate and full bittersweet blends are an acquired taste. Many people used to uniformity of commercial products, criticise farmhouse ciders for their unpredictability. But this is part of their charm, reflecting as it does, the variability of the orchards and the countryside.

Farmhouse ciders, good to excellent, still hold their place in West Country industry, as an important local product to be sought out by tourists and devotees. There is no place here to list all the farm cider-makers worth a visit, but to mention just a few at random. Ben Crossman of Hewish, learnt the art from his grandfather who 'graduated' from a year at Long Ashton in the

1920s, and he makes excellent farmhouse cider from fruit picked in his own orchards just off the road to Weston-super-Mare.

For those not acquainted with the ambience of West Country life, what better initiation experience could there be than a visit to Roger Wilkins at Lands End Farm, Mudgely, for a taste of true Somerset farmhouse cider. It may be a draughty old barn but it is just the right temperature for the fermentation, and those who visit in the autumn will have a chance to see the cider press in action. Roger took over the business from his grandfather who started pressing in 1917. He still has a few of his own orchards but remembers when the whole of the Wedmore ridge was covered with cider apples.

Down towards Highbridge at Watchfield is a small cider industry which is undergoing a renaissance of its own. Martin Rich, following in his uncle's footsteps, is building up a reputation for a quality product, a taste which owes much to the good assortment of fruit he harvests from the traditional orchards nearby. Not far away down the lanes at Mark, is Chris Coombes whose farm cider museum gives a little extra for the visitor to see. All his draught ciders are matured in oak barrels as they have been since the family business began in 1919. Now he makes a particularly robust Kingston Black cider as well as perry from genuine perry pears. At nearby Brent Knoll are two more makers producing good quality farmhouse cider from local orchards; at Dobunni Fruit Farm on the road to Brean, and West Croft Farm near the Post Office.

Other small scale cider-makers have started making single variety ciders, a trend which is catching-on and becoming fashionable as the public taste becomes more educated and discriminating. The range currently available in Somerset includes; Morgan Sweet, Dabinett, Tremletts Bitter, Stoke Red, Somerset Redstreak and of course, the legendary Kingston Black. Heck's of Street produce a pasteurised Kingston Black, a clear, stable and dry, bottled cider, easily portable and with a popular taste.

Most makers will tell you that farmhouse cider sales are down, drastically down from a few years ago, partly though the ease of supermarket shopping for inexpensive mass-produced drink, but mainly through our changing tastes as we become a more affluent society, able to afford expensive, more 'sophisticated' products like European wines. Some of the cider-makers have risen to meet this opposition by producing new cider products, innovative and enticing in tasteful packaging.

Perry's Cider in Dowlish Wake, near Ilminster, a family business housed in its ancient mill buildings with plenty of diversions and distractions, is well worth a visit. Perry's have 17 acres of their own of orchards and buy in fruit from many farms round about. They have produced award winning traditional cider for many years, but now are offering something more to meet the challenge, traditional cider, crystal clear, polished and bottled, an up-market product with a sophisticated taste that still maintains its 'country feel'. The quality single variety ciders made from Somerset Redstreak and Morgan Sweet are bottled at 6%.

Once cider-making is increased to a large commercial scale, the more difficult it becomes to achieve this level of excellence. It is inevitable that as output is increased, the larger raw material requirement means that fruit usually has to come from more variable sources. It is more difficult to select and monitor quality, and impossible to optimise the timing of the harvesting and processing. These disadvantages of scale are off-set by greater uniformity and stability of the average product which can be achieved by the batch processing. The larger companies are also able to indulge in better presentation, a major selling advantage.

Matthew Clark in Shepton Mallet is an amalgam of Taunton Cider, Showerings, Coates, Gamer's, Whiteways and many other smaller firms. Their well known products are distributed internationally and range from those designed to compete with lagers and beers, to an excellent traditional cider made from selected cider apples which rivals the best farmhouse cider. A few years ago when the factory was occupied by Showerings, their orcharding manager, Geoff Rowson joined forces with cider apple experts, Les Davis and Tony Calder, and scoured the old orchards to save some of the rarer varieties. They brought them together and planted a museum orchard at Shepton Mallet, now owned, cherished and protected by Matthew Clark's chief executive, Peter Aikens.

Many of the old farms that once used to make their own cider now take their fruit to the mill at Shepton Mallet. A large number of growers with traditional orchards maintain their loyalty to Matthew Clark as fruit suppliers, originally having sold their fruit to Showerings before the take-over. The farmer's role has become fruit grower, raw material producer for the cider industry and no longer cider-maker. Their future is assured while the trees remain in good condition and the orchards large enough to produce a reasonable quantity of fruit annually. The company is actively encouraging their growers in sound maintenance practices to keep their orchards economically viable and stocked with genuine cider apple varieties. Much of the factory's demand is supplied by the company's own contract growers, many of whom originally planted their bush orchards for Taunton Cider way back in the 1970s, but recently with the soaring popularity of cider nationally, they have had to launch a huge planting scheme.

The prospects for the future of our Somerset orchards should be rosy while cider sales go up and up. At this time, standard trees are easily available off-the-peg in a wide range of varieties and both Somerset County Council and the Countryside Commission offer incentives and grants for replanting and orchard stewardship. They not only recognise the amenity value of traditional orchards in the countryside, but remember that the cider-making industry is an integral part of the history and heritage of the county. Naturally, only true Somerset cider apple varieties are approved for their replanting schemes.

Another Somerset success story is Thatcher's Cider at Sandford in the north of the county. Expanding almost overnight from a small family business supplying a local market of Bristol and the surrounding area to a hugely successful high-profile cider-maker and processor for the whole of the industry, Thatcher's has made a significant contribution to the rise in popularity of the product and to the confidence of the cider-making trade. Limited by the restrictions of large scale production, the majority of their products are typically commercial with a broad appeal, but happily, traditional farmhouse cider is made and sold in their shop in reassuring quantities. They also make an interesting range of single variety ciders, including Morgan Sweet, Tremletts Bitter, Somerset Redstreak and best of all Dabinett. There are several acres of orchards in the village near the cider mill, one with a collection of over 300 apple varieties, many of them ciders. Some fifty acres of their new bush orchards line the motorway where the M5 passes through Mendip near Crook Peak.

Sheppy's Cider at Bradford on Tone, not far from Taunton, uses a traditional blend of fruit to make their farmhouse cider, as draught or filtered and bottled. David Sheppy still makes the two original lines, the slightly sparkling Bullfinch (medium) and Goldfinch (dry), both a mixture of draught and vintage cider, as his father Richard and grandfather did before him. Richard planted five acres of Kingston Black bush trees nearly twenty years ago with the intention of making a single variety cider. Now this range is extended to Tremlett's Bitter and Dabinett, filtered and pasteurised and bottled at 7.2%. These single varieties are now their best selling lines.

Sheppy's have been producing award winning ciders for decades, since collecting the coveted Gold Medal at the 1930 International Brewing Exhibition, a feather in the cap for a small scale cider-maker in open competition. The exhibition is long since discontinued but their traditional show cider is still made with home-grown Tremlett's Bitter, Yarlington Mill, Harry Masters and Chisel Jersey bittersweets, lightened and sharpened with Stoke Red and Kingston Black, and bottled at 8%. This class of cider owes its origins to the original work at Butleigh and the NFCI.

Those keen cider-makers in the early 1900s who were party to the experiments being done by the experts, began to compete with one another to make superior cider, the 'show cider', of a quality perhaps surpassed by only a few today. The process necessitated great care and personal attention at all stages, and years of experience in the choice of the material and its treatment. Just the right vintage apples blended in just the right proportions had to be harvested at the optimum time and brought with care to the mill. The varieties and the proportions of each that they used were closely guarded secrets, mentioned only in trusted family circles. The cider-making process itself was conducted with great skill and close attention to cleanliness to guarantee that the fermentation process proceeded in the most favourable way to the potential 'champion' product.

The introduction of filtration to remove yeasts and stabilise the cider with some residual sugars, made it possible to take the 'rough' edge off the taste by retaining a degrees of sweetness. The standard of those ciders at the turn of the century was often exceptional, despite the primitive methods used. The publicity and general acclaim that the best 'show' ciders received at the major agricultural shows brought quality cider back into the public interest, from which the more commercial cider factories began to benefit.

Now at the start of the twenty-first century, we are witnessing the beginning of a second renaissance. Cider is rising again from its humble origins and bringing with it all the best flavours and images, the essence and aromas of the orchard. The driving force behind its ascension is the necessity to charm the customer back to the produce of the apple, now transformed, transcended from 'just cider' into a whole new world of stylish, sophisticated innovations.

The ingenuity of the 'new craftsmen' of the cider world lies in the rediscovery and practice of some of the oldest skills. Julian Temperley of Burrow Hill, near Kingsbury Episcopi, the creator of the Somerset Cider Brandy Company, is responsible for unlocking the secrets of apple brandy for us all on this side of the Channel. The excellent Somerset Royal and Somerset five-year-old brandy are accompanied by an apple aperitif made from a blend of cider brandy and the juice of Kingston Black.

There is another secret practice going on in the Burrow Hill cellar, the creation of a sparkling bottled cider made by the *méthode champenoise*. Fully dry cider is bottled with sugar and a little champagne yeast, corked and wired, and laid on its side for a month or two. After being placed neck down in a rack, each bottle is gently shaken every day to settle the yeast deposit in the neck so that it can be 'disgorged' as a plug before final corking. This process, an English one, was used freely to bottle wine and cider as long ago as 1650, even before the birth of French sparkling wine. For all these products, genuine cider apples are a prerequisite raw material and Burrow Hill boasts of the largest traditional standard orchards in the South West. They roll over more than 130 acres and contain many interesting, truly local varieties.

Who knows what exciting and imaginative elaborations the future will bring, but while the enthusiasm to make them is sustained and their fame spreads ever far and wide, so the future of our English cider orchard is secured. We are on the brink of an exciting renaissance of the cider industry. Will history repeat itself in time for our orchards?

THE BITTER WITH THE SWEET

There are those who claim that cider can be made from any old apples. But Somerset's cider-makers know better. It is true that yeast needs sugar for fermentation, and true that all apples contain sugar and have an appley sort of flavour. But this only makes a mild sort of fermented apple juice and not a proper cider. The pioneering work done at Butleigh by Neville Grenville and Lloyd, and the selection of vintage quality varieties at Long Ashton, is testimony to that.

Real bittersweet cider apples have an additional, exclusive element in their juice make-up, tannin. Tannin is a collective term for a group of naturally occurring phenolic compounds with complicated molecular structures. But their contribution to cider is simply to give it that rounded full flavour and body, and impart the lovely golden colour. These are qualities not tasted in cider made from 'any old apples'.

True cider apples, bittersweet apples, have never really existed in any quantity outside the South West and the West Midlands although there is a remarkable revival of interest at present and cider orchards are now being planted in the traditional dessert apple areas of Kent and Sussex.

All our apples, eaters, cookers and ciders, come from a common origin, the wild apples or *Malus*. After centuries of selection and cultivation by man, we literally have thousands of apples for every purpose to choose from; all shapes and sizes, large and small, all shades of green-red-yellow, and many different flavours. True West Country bittersweet cider apples are closest to their wild ancestors. Their juice retains the natural

Storing cider fruit in willow hurdle pens for the early trials at the Cider Institute. Washed cloths for the cider press 'cheeses' hang in the trees behind.

tannins of some of the *Malus* and their taste is astringent and at first unpalatable. But a disagreeable taste is a useful anti-scrumping asset in a farm orchard. Maybe that is why cider apples, the reddest and most shiny, were often planted temptingly by the hedge and which, once sampled, discouraged further interest in the trees beyond, however tasty.

Tannins evolved in ancestral apples as part of their natural plant defence mechanisms. When the skin of an apple is broken, say by insect damage, the juice flows and is exposed to the air. Phenolic compounds are easily oxidised and the flesh quickly turns brown. The thick brown oxidised juice blocks and closes the wound, in much the same way that blood clots to seal a cut, and the fruit is protected from further damage. Some of these compounds are strongly fungistatic, that is, they discourage the growth of fungal diseases that attack apple trees. This is of course a useful evolutionary attribute for survival of the fittest.

The cider apple phenolic compounds between them contribute to the golden colour, the traditional flavour, the 'body' and 'mouth-feel' of real cider. The colour develops as the juice oxidises when the apples are pressed, and usually deepens as the drink matures. Phloridzin, a tannin unique to apples, oxidises to bright yellow in air, but it is the oxidation products of the procyanidins which are responsible for much of the colour of cider. Procyanidins are true tannins and can impart a taste which is either soft and bitter or harsh and astringent, depending on the size of their molecules.

For example, Tremletts Bitter has a 'hard' tannin and the flavour of its cider is bitter, catching the back of the tongue. It is an acquired taste appreciated by some, but Tremletts is much better blended with other varieties for a more generally acceptable and balanced product. Dabinett on the other hand has a softer tasting tannin with a gentler and more pleasing impact. Dabinett makes an excellent unblended, single variety cider. It is this bitterness or astringency that is so excitingly and refreshingly different about the characteristic Somerset cider flavour.

In addition, real cider might actually be good for us. A group of phenolic compounds found in apples, the flavanoids, are receiving some current acclaim for their health giving properties. There is a growing body of medical opinion that these flavanoids can have beneficial effects in the prevention and treatment of human diseases, including cardio-vascular disease and cancer. Producers of red wine and tea have claimed their products contain important levels of flavanoids, but it is likely that cider apples are an even richer source. Another reason for making cider with real cider apples!

Not all cider apples are bittersweets, rich in both tannin and sugar. Some have little or no tannin, just flavour and sugar. These are termed sweets or pure sweets. The well known and much loved Morgan Sweet is a pure sweet, as are Taylor's Sweet, Dunkerton's Late, Woodbine and many others. On their own they make a thin but interesting cider and are usually best blended with bittersweets.

The most common acidic juice component peculiar to apples, for eating, cooking or cider making, is malic acid. Cider apples rich in acid, more than 0.45%, but low or lacking in tannin are classed as sharps. Our farm orchards also contain a motley collection of cooking and eating apples, together with those useful varieties termed loosely, dual purpose. These sorts are generally quite sharp, with malic acid from 0.45-0.8% or even 1.0%. Their acidity is culinary in its character, rather than vintage quality, a difference difficult to describe without tasting a few apples to compare the flavours. They are traditionally multi-purpose, being suitable for cooking early in the season, then for eating as the acidity mellows with keeping, and finally, when they are no longer fit for the kitchen, ready for the cider press.

Names like Tom Putt, Crimson King and the ancient variety Stubbard have lived in old orchards and contributed to farm cider for centuries. But there are also many true cider sharps, selected, valued and cherished, like Gin or Backwell Red and Black Vallis, natives of north Somerset. These have special 'vintage' qualities to raise the drink out of the ordinary. In Devon and spilling over the border into Somerset, locally bred sharps are quite common in the old orchards and have a significant influence on the characteristic, more acidic flavour of Devon cider.

Those cider apples that combine tannin with their acidity are known as bittersharps and, like the bittersweet apples they have more than 0.2% tannin. This type of cider apple is more peculiar to south and central Somerset where some excellent bittersharps of character have originated, such as the legendary Kingston Black. This variety yields a balanced juice and, in a good year, can produce a cider with a pleasing blend of bitterness, acidity and sweetness, alone without blending. But there are others, like the exceptional Stoke Red and Porter's Perfection, selected with perfect balance in mind. Closely related Stembridge Clusters and Lambrook Pippin also once had some reputation. There are a number of bittersharps with penetrating acidity which originated in Hereford and Gloucestershire and some of their offspring have been born and brought up in Somerset.

True cider apples have yet another unique property, their texture. They are not crisp or crunchy to the bite. They are woolly and everlastingly chewy, as anyone who tries to eat one will discover. The farmers of the old days were clever enough to appreciate this woolly-ness as a virtue, for it boosts apple press-ability enormously. Even in modern pressing mills with heavy hydraulic equipment, eating apples like Cox's are slippery and difficult to press efficiently. Their arrival at the cider press is greeted with groans. Whatever the method of extraction, woolly textured cider apples are more stable and yield greater quantities of juice. Centuries of horse-powered stone crushing must have led to this piece of evolution by selection of the most manageable varieties under difficult conditions.

Although most of our cider apples are not much more than one or two hundred years old, there are a few which are clearly ancient, seventeenth century or before. Stubbard is one, an old codlin type, closely resembling a wild apple. The name Stubbard may have originated from 'stub' or 'stump', referring to their ability, in common with many truly old apples, to root from cuttings. Royal Wildling is of ancient origin. Wildling is another name for a seedling. The trees that are called Royal Wildling in Herefordshire are said to be the same as those we call Cadbury in Somerset. They may not be identical but perhaps have derived from Wildling seedlings themselves.

Many names are clearly descriptive; Hangdown with its weeping tree habit; Broadleaf; Silver Cup with its broad, deep eye basin; Sheep's Nose, there are many shaped like this; Bell and Lady's Finger, longer than it is broad. Bishop's Nose is intriguing. Perhaps it was long and red, but it is sadly lost without a description. Although he disappeared in 1895, the Bishop must have had a sharp tongue; his juice was recorded in the Bath and West Show list as very acid!

Many bear the name to carry the fame of the originator like Tremlett's Bitter, Ellis Bitter, Dabinett, Dunkerton's Late, Brown's Apple and Harry Masters' Jersey. Porter's Perfection records the success of nurseryman, Charles Porter of Lambrook, and is an excellent tasting variety. Many are named after the village or place where they came from; Kingston Black (Kingston St Mary, near Taunton), Lambrook Pippin, Stoke Red (after Rodney Stoke), Gatcombe (near Long Ashton), Yarlington Mill, and many others. Ashton Brown Jersey and Ashton Bitter were named in honour of the Research Station.

Other names are more romantic, such as the pale and blushing Fair Maid of Taunton, also called Moonshines. Being blond, she

Checking the fermentation rate in the experimental sheds at Long Ashton. The casks are fitted with fermentation locks to exclude air.

shows up well in the dark, and harvesting can go on after work in the short autumn days. Hoary Morning has a waxy bloom on its cheeks like a coating of frost, but is also mischievously called Bachelor's Glory! Tom Putt sometimes has a strange bluish, meaty bloom which may account for its synonym, Marrowbone. Sops in Wine is a very old apple with a name descriptive of its dark red skin blotched with milk. It is easy to see how Ten Commandments gets its name. When the apple is cut in half, there are ten red dots around the core, from the ten red veins running through the white flesh.

Unfortunately, Fillbarrel's name is less appropriate. It has a reputation for being very biennial, and so fills the barrels only every other year. Poor Man's Profit is wistful but perhaps optimistic. Never-Deceive-Me or Seek-No-Further are names of integrity, and Truckle and Buskin conjure a pleasant rustic picture. Alas, many of these apples are lost from memory now.

Some names describe the properties of the juice, like Sharp Shooter, a viciously acidic apple with some tannin. Tom Tanners was reputed to be devastatingly astringent and used only sparingly. Other names suggest outstanding vintage qualities, such as Gin or Port Wine, and Porter's Perfection still has a reputation for producing an excellent cider. Some names extol other virtues of the cider made from them, particularly the effect on the human digestive system. Runaway, Slack-ma-Girdle, Burstout and Little Trotts leave little to the imagination.

In the early part of the twentieth century, when the Cider Institute advertised for growers to submit their favourite cider apples for judging, there was much competition for the annual cider making prizes. Many of the apples must have been seedlings, often hastily named before sending in, and often bearing the name of the sender in the hope of fame, like Jenning's Seedling. Some may have been sent in with incorrect names which later proved to be distinct varieties, leading to much confusion and perpetuation of mistakes. Synonyms often arose through the need to invent a name for one lost or forgotten. Sometimes known varieties were hijacked and given a false name for the sake of finding a 'new variety' with guaranteed merit. Incorrect synonyms also arose through spelling mistakes, or from copying down names phonetically, especially when delivered in a broad Somerset accent.

The name which takes the prize for extreme obscurity must be Loyal Drain! This apple is the well known Red Jersey, sent to Long Ashton on many occasions labelled 'Laurel Grange', the name of the farm in West Pennard where it came from. After this misnomer, Red Jersey was known for quite some time as Loyal Drang, Loral Drain or any combination of those names. During the first half of the last century, most of these discrepancies were sorted out, and varieties with any vintage promise were collected and grown at Long Ashton or in trial orchards around the counties.

Some cider apples bear a 'Royal' name, such as Court Royal, Royal Jersey and Royal Wildling. There could be two reasons for this. It may simply be that the cider prepared from them was considered so exceptional that it was fit for royalty. But in these 'Royal' apples, the eye of sepals is curiously erect and resembles a tiny pointed crown. A fanciful mark of superiority perhaps.

Then there are the 'improved' apples. If a cider variety had a fault, its popularity might wane, but there have always been plenty of enthusiastic amateur horticulturists ready to try a little propagation in the hope of improving on the original. A rash of 'new varieties' was created at the height of the Cider Institute activity during the early part of the twentieth century. Dove is one that was tinkered with, leading to Stone Dove, Dove Seedling and others. These would have been selected from seedlings grown from the pomace and therefore similar to the parent. Improved Dove did have some real improvements, but the experiment was not always successful. Improved Kingston Black is certainly not a change for the better, being very different but having greatly inferior vintage qualities to its forbear.

There has always been much discussion about the origins of the group of bittersweet apples known as 'jerseys'. These are of Somerset origin and were sometimes referred to as 'georges', named after a brown earthenware vessel used for carrying cider in the past. There was once speculation that 'jersey' was a corruption of the word 'jaisy', meaning bitter in Somerset dialect, but this has never been substantiated. Although it was once thought that these apples originally came from the island of Jersey, it is most unlikely. There are many traditional Jersey bittersweets, some similar to their Breton counterparts, but none are the same as any of our 'jerseys'.

Since there was once much trading of fruit from the Channel Islands for cider-making in times of shortage on the mainland, Jersey bittersweet apples must have gained a good reputation. Perhaps the taste, now so characteristic to Somerset cider, was first acquired in those days. So our 'jerseys' may have come to us indirectly from the island that shares their name. It is reasonable to imagine that they began as seedlings grown from the pomace waste thrown out after pressing imported fruit, and were brought up as natives. Certainly in the latter part of the nineteenth century, many French bittersweet varieties were introduced with the intention of improving the standards of our cider. None of these are called 'jerseys', nor are they much like our 'jerseys' either. Although more common in the West Midlands, they do crop up in some of the old Somerset orchards that were planted in the twentieth century. Those that do not have French names are recognised as 'Normans', such as Bulmer's, White, Cherry, Sherrington Norman and many others.

Now, in the twenty-first century, Somerset has a fine collection of 'jerseys'; Chisel Jersey, Broadleaf, Coat, Red and Royal, Stable and Stembridge Jerseys, White Jersey and Harry Masters' Jersey – named after the miller at Yarlington Mill. And how did Chisel Jersey get its name? Chesil is an old English name for a pebble; and a small, hard, russeted Chisel Jersey apple is about as appetising as a stone!

PART 2

THE DESCRIPTIONS

ASHTON BITTER
Early Full Bittersweet

A seedling raised from a Dabinett x Stoke Red cross by Mr G.T. Spinks, plant breeder at Long Ashton in the 1950s, and carrying many of the attributes of both varieties. It was resurrected in the 1980s by the late Geoff Potter, then Orcharding Manager at H.P. Bulmer, from an old trial orchard where it had been cropping well. Ashton Bitter was widely planted during the 1990s as an early harvesting variety for intensive bush orchards, spreading the harvesting season into late September.

The bushy head is made up of weak, whippy lateral branches covered in numerous greyish-green, willowy leaves, making it difficult to train to ideal bush tree shape. It is hard to maintain a centre leader as it is inclined to carry fruit and bend over. Ashton Bitter needs a strong rootstock on poor soils and is not suited to a windy site. Flowering late May with Dabinett and Stoke Red, it needs a pollinator variety close by. The apples mature in late September or early October and are highly coloured, bright orange-red and glossy when ripe. They tend to crop biennially and are born in clusters which can push the centre fruit off prematurely in September.

Size: Medium to large, 55 to more than 60mm.
Shape: Conical, rounded; regular, tending to ribbed; king fruits common.
Stem: Thick and projecting distinctly from a small and shallow basin; fleshy and often strigged in king fruit.
Eye: Basin small, narrow and deep, rather irregular or beaded; sepals fairly long but often broken, reflexed at tips.
Skin: Golden yellow; smooth, waxy or greasy; russet none or very little near stem; lenticels inconspicuous.
Flush: Always more than 75%, orange diffuse flecked and speckled bright red.
Flesh: Full bittersweet; yellowish, juicy and chewy.
Core: Proximal, relatively small; seeds number variable, often few; tube large, deep, usually open to core.
Juice: SG 1060.
Cider: The juice is full bittersweet with plenty of astringency and aroma, producing a useful blending cider with rather strong tannin.

ASHTON BROWN JERSEY
Late Medium Bittersweet
Synonym: Brown Jersey.

This typical Somerset 'jersey' apple was found as an un-named variety in an old cider orchard in Long Ashton village in the early 1900s. In its preliminary trials it was called Ashton No.32. It was properly named later when its vintage cider making characteristics became recognised, but it never achieved popularity as an orchard tree because it is so slow to come into cropping. It was planted in a few old standard and bush trial orchards in both Hereford and Somerset.

Ashton Brown Jersey forms a medium sized tree with a compact head. It is fairly scab resistant and once it comes into cropping, it is quite regular. Flowering is mid-season.

The fruit matures late, from the second week of November onwards. It is rather small, regular shaped, dark red and russeted.

Size: Medium, rather small, 45-55mm.
Shape: Blunt nosed, conical, tending towards cylindrical; regular.
Stem: Often fleshy, projecting slightly or level with the base; stem basin regular, usually shallow but sometimes deep.
Eye: Basin shallow or slight, slightly puckered or trace of a beading; calyx closed or slightly open, sepals reflexed, sometimes green.
Skin: Yellow or yellowish-green to golden yellow or orange; overall rough and dull; light russet often considerable, spreading in a network, but sometimes only in the stem basin; lenticels conspicuous, often very large and irregular especially round the stem.
Flush: Always more than 35% often more then 65%, flecked or slightly striped, rarely diffuse only, dark red flecks and stripes.
Flesh: Sweet and astringent; yellowish or white, sometimes greenish; woolly.
Core: Slightly proximal, usually axile, loculi small, slightly open; seeds numerous, large, brown, filling loculi; tube conical; stamens median.
Juice: SG 1054; acidity 0.14%; tannin 0.23%.
Cider: Ashton Brown Jersey produces a good, full-bodied cider, soft and medium bittersweet.

BACKWELL RED
Mid Season Sharp

At the beginning of the twentieth century this variety was widely grown in North Somerset and is named after the village of Backwell, where it probably still exists as old trees. Early trials at the Cider Institute confirmed its vintage value and many trees were distributed in county trial orchards. It has since lost favour owing to its irregular cropping, though it may be more reliable when grown as a bush tree.

Mature standard trees are medium sized with a neat compact head, but are slightly scab susceptible. Bush trees can be very vigorous and spreading. Spurring is rather sparse with much bare wood. Cropping is slow to establish and rather biennial, but good. It flowers early mid-season, late April to early May, is diploid and a good pollinator.

Although the fruit matures fairly early, from the second week of October, it is often difficult to shake off the trees until late October. The milling period is up to three weeks. The fruit is medium sized, roundish, red and yellow and characterised by a long stem in a curiously flattened, one-sided stem basin.

Size: Small, often medium, 40-50mm.
Shape: Conical or tending to cylindrical, rarely tending to round; regular.
Stem: Projecting distinctly or considerably, thin and woody and sometimes offset; stem basin medium, often deep and characteristically flattened on one side.
Eye: Basin medium, puckered, sometimes ribbed, sometimes irregular and beaded, occasionally flattened on one side; calyx slightly open or closed, sepals fairly long and reflexed but usually broken.
Skin: Pale yellow or greenish-yellow; smooth and slightly waxy; rarely rough and scaly russet spreading across the cheek; lenticels sometimes conspicuous.
Flush: Always present, usually more than 75%, often more or less complete, diffuse red flecked and slightly striped.
Flesh: Acidic with no astringency; white, usually reddened under the skin and in the vascular bundles; soft and juicy.
Core: Median, axile, usually closed loculi; tube a rather deep cone; stamens distal.
Juice: SG 1051; acidity 0.70%; tannin 0.13%.
Cider: Backwell Red cider at best is good, sharp, light and fruity. It can often be rather thin and of average quality and is best blended. Fermentation is moderately slow.

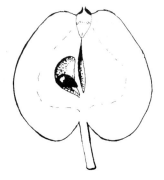

BELL APPLE
Mid Season Sweet
Synonym: Sweet Sheep's Nose.

It is its distinctive shape that gives this Somerset sweet apple its name. Bell Apple or Sweet Sheep's Nose is one of many Sheep's Noses, but is different enough to be distinguished as a distinct variety with its dark mauve flush and sweet taste. Bell was first recorded at the RHS Exhibition in 1883 and it was quite often sent to Long Ashton from central Somerset, where it may have arisen. Bell makes a useful cider with good flavour and aroma, and was therefore quite a popular choice in old farm orchards. It still occurs as old trees throughout central and southern Somerset.

Mature Bell trees are quite large and upright but tend to droop with heavy crops. Flowering time is late April or early May. The apples are distinctive, large and green, conical, with a broad, flat base and a stubby stalk. They are ready for harvest in late October.

Size: Often large to very large but varying with crop, 45mm to more than 60mm.
Shape: Conical, base broad and flat, usually slightly 'waisted' giving the shape of an inverted bell; smoothly ribbed or angular.
Stem: Stout stub within a broad, deep stem cavity, occasionally projecting slightly.
Eye: Basin small but well defined, smooth; calyx open, sepals free, upright, distinctive.
Skin: Pale green; smooth, dry; russet light in the stem basin; lenticels with pale surround.
Flush: Usually 50-75%, speckled and flecked pinkish mauve to red.
Flesh: Mild sweet; chewy; greenish; vascular strands appear as green lines in section.
Core: Open; tube a deep cone or funnel; stamens distal.
Juice: SG 1058, acidity 0.18%, tannin 0.12%.
Cider: Long Ashton cider trials describe Bell as a very useful sweet cider with good flavour and aroma, good alone or blended. Fermentation is slow.

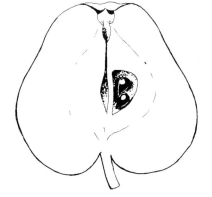

BROADLEAF JERSEY
Late Bittersweet
Synonym: Broadleaves.

Broadleaf Jersey was widely planted in the beginning of the twentieth century throughout Somerset to the Dorset border. Its cider was first judged for the Bath and West Show in 1895. It is a variety that was often used as a stem builder but it has no particular merit for cider making and is no longer sought after. It is just possible that Broadleaf Jersey, under its old name Broadleaves, was one of the original Paradise rootstocks from which all the modern rootstocks have originated. Several, notably M26, do have bittersweet fruit.

The trees are large with a slightly spreading habit. It is very susceptible to canker and the leaves and fruit are prone to scab. Flowering is late mid season in May and cropping is irregular.

Broadleaf Jersey is a late maturing November apple of medium size, with a distinctly waisted conical shape in an unappetising dark green with a brownish flush.

Size: Large, 55 to more than 60mm.
Shape: Conical, elongated distinct nose, base rounded.
Stem: Stout, woody, projecting slightly or distinctly from a broad, shallow basin.
Eye: Basin shallow, narrow, distinctly puckered, tending to crowned; sepals closed and upright.
Skin: Dark heavy green; shiny; scab susceptible.
Flush: Often only a very slight brownish trace of flush spreading from stem basin to cheek.
Flesh: Bittersweet, greenish and chewy.
Core: Axile, median, small; tube often a deep cone.
Juice: SG 1054, acidity 0.26%, tannin 0.30%.
Cider: Broadleaf Jersey cider is reported to be thin, dry, rather bitter and of indifferent to moderate quality only suitable for blending. Sugar content is moderate but fermentation rather rapid.

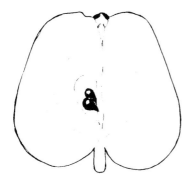

BROWN'S APPLE
Early Sharp

This apple was bred at Hill's Nursery, near Staverton in Devon, probably in the early part of the twentieth century. It was one of several similar varieties intended for traditional Devon orchards; clean, fresh tasting sharps. Brown's Apple is similar to its brother, Nelson. Both are, or were until recently, free from scab. For this reason, Brown's Apple has also been popular in Somerset both for replanting old orchards and for use in more recent bush orchards where it has been extensively planted in the late 1990s as a trouble-free, early maturing variety. It is commonly seen now in all counties and is capable of phenomenal crops, even if biennially.

Young trees are slow to start growth in the first year or so, but once established, become very vigorous with many rather upright primary branches. They can be prone to canker and mildew. Spurring is slow with some bare wood in the first years. Brown's Apple flowers mid season. Blossom is bold but slow to develop. Standard trees are medium sized with a slightly spreading, neat head.

The apples are distinctive; bright red, rather broad and flattened and quite a generous size. It is a first quality sharp apple but was not always classed as a cider apple in the past, and has not always commanded a premium price. This is happily not the case with the modern contract bush orchards where it is welcomed.

Size: Medium to large, 45-60mm plus.
Shape: Oblate or flattened cylindrical, broad; regular.
Stem: Thick, fleshy, often strigged, often off-set, projecting distinctly from a deep, steep basin.
Eye: Basin medium, smooth with a trace of ribs; calyx slightly open, sepals long, pubescent.
Skin: Yellow, shiny, waxy; russet absent.
Flush: Always, more than 65%, often almost complete; heavy diffuse, flecked and striped dark red.
Flesh: Mild sharp, white, chewy.
Core: Medium, open, axile; tube broad.
Juice: SG 1048; acidity 0.67%; tannin 0.12%.
Cider: Brown's Apple makes a very good sharp cider, fresh and clean, with a fruity aroma.

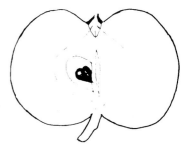

BROWN SNOUT
Late Bittersweet

Brown Snout is a Hereford variety sometimes seen in orchards in Somerset. It is said to have originated on a farm at Yarkhill in the middle of the nineteenth century. It is now widely distributed in the West Midlands since it has been propagated and distributed by Bulmers. It was also included in the 1952 series of bush tree trial orchards in all the cider growing counties. Because of its late flowering habit, it is useful for low-lying areas or frost pockets, and is more often than not, found growing alongside Vilberie as a pollinator.

Mature trees are medium sized with upright growth. The apples, which mature late, in the first half of November, are similar to Michelin. The two varieties are easy to separate. Michelin is by far the most commonly grown cider variety, usually in association with Dabinett, and its fruits are quite elongated and angular. Brown Snout, is much less frequently encountered. Its fruit have a distinctive russet patch around the eye, and are a regular conical shape without ribs.

Size: Small, rarely medium, 40-55mm.
Shape: Conical, rarely rounded or cylindrical.
Stem: Thin, woody, projecting slightly from a medium sized, narrow basin.
Eye: Basin absent or slight; calyx closed, sepals touching, short, reflexed at tip.
Skin: Yellow-green, smooth slightly waxy; russet at stem and eye, sometimes slightly spreading to cheek; lenticels sometimes small brown dots.
Flush: Rarely a slight pinkish-orange diffuse.
Flesh: Sweet with slight astringency; white, soft, dry.
Core: Slightly distal, axile, open; tube conical, rarely a funnel, deep.
Juice: SG 1053; acidity 0.24%; tannin 0.24%.
Cider: Mild to medium bittersweet; soft astringent tannin, average quality.

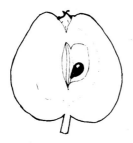

BULMER'S NORMAN
Early Bittersweet

When Bulmer's Cider Company began to establish orchards in the early twentieth Century, Bulmer's Norman was one of the many trees that they imported from France. It was un-named but because of its outstanding orchard performance, it was propagated and widely distributed as 'Bulmer's Norman'. It is now grown throughout the West Country and is one of the best, most frequently used stembuilders. Because of its vigour, this variety sometimes out-grows the top worked variety and it is not uncommon to see tree canopies, part Bulmer's Norman, part a weaker variety, or totally taken over by Bulmer's Norman. It occurs commonly in its own right throughout Somerset, mostly in standard orchards.

Bulmer's Norman trees are often easy to spot; large, very vigorous and spreading, often with a span of up to 40 feet, and with large, distinctive leaves. It flowers early mid-season but is a triploid and therefore a poor pollinator.

Its apples, often disfigured and distorted with scab, are usually large, broadly conical and plain yellow-green. They mature in the first half of October and do not keep at all well, especially in the off-year when they can be very large and thin skinned.

Size: Medium to large, 55 to more than 60mm.
Shape: Conical sometimes flattened; somewhat irregular.
Stem: Thin, woody, projecting slightly, sometimes distinctly, sometimes level with base; stem basin very wide and deep.
Eye: Basin often very deep, usually irregular, sometimes puckered.
Skin: Yellow to green; smooth, slightly waxy; russet usually confined to stem basin, rarely spreading to cheek; lenticels sometimes conspicuous.
Flush: Rare, sometimes a slight orange diffuse.
Flesh: Sweet with full tannin, green, woolly.
Core: Median; tube usually conical.
Juice: SG 1053; acidity 0.24%; tannin 0.27%.
Cider: Medium bittersweet; hard and bitter tannin. Fast fermenting juice.

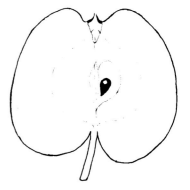

BURROW HILL EARLY
Early Bittersweet

In the search in the 1980s for early maturing cider varieties with potential for bush orchards, Burrow Hill Early was rediscovered by Julian Temperley of Burrow Hill Cider, from an old orchard nearby. Its true title was not known so it was renamed after the Burrow Hill itself, a local landmark next to the Cider House at Stembridge in Somerset. It was propagated by Long Ashton for use in bush orchards but was never widely adopted because it is slow to come into cropping and rather biennial. It still exists as old trees and in a few recent trial orchards.

Bush trees are vigorous and spreading with much bare wood. Flowering is mid season.

The fruits, which look very similar to Red Worthy, can be distinguished from this variety by their shorter stems and earlier maturity. Burrow Hill Early is ready by the end of September or early October to make a useful to start the pressing season. The apples are covered with a strong red flush, conical and medium sized.

Size: Medium, 40-55mm.
Shape: Rounded conical with a broad flat base.
Stem: Within or protruding slightly from a small shallow basin.
Eye: Basin shallow, slightly puckered or smooth; sepals closed or slightly open.
Skin: Pale yellow; smooth and waxy; lenticels surrounded by light patches on the flush near the stem end; russet occasionally spreading over the cheek.
Flush: Always more than 60%, flecked and slightly striped, bright red.
Flesh: Sweet and astringent; white, dry, chewy, soft.
Core: Large, axile, usually closed, loculi flat but large; tube deep and wide; stamens high in tube.
Juice: Full bittersweet. SG 1055.
Cider: Burrow Hill Early makes an excellent full bodied, early bittersweet cider with a very fruity aroma and fair tannin. It is said to be useful alone or for blending with inferior ciders.

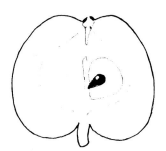

BUTTERY DOOR
Early Multipurpose
Synonyms: Buttery D'or/Do/Dough.

Buttery Door fruit was first sent to the Cider Institute in 1926 by Mr Warren, cider maker of Netherbury in Dorset. The resultant cider was described as 'fair, with an aromatic flavour'. It is often described as a pastry apple, one suited to making apple dumplings, sharp and flavoured. Trees probably still exist in old orchards in south Somerset and neighbouring Dorset. Thanks to a Mrs Scott Daniel from Dorset who recognised the fruit from one good old tree near Bridport, Buttery Door has recently been repropagated and is available in nurseries again.

Buttery Door is a good sized, rather flattened, firm, pale green or golden, mildly sharp apple.

Size: Medium to large, often more than 60mm.
Shape: Oblate; often lopsided, angular or tending to ribbed.
Stem: Medium to short, woody, within a medium cavity, broad and deep.
Eye: Basin small, deep, rather irregular, occasionally beaded; sepals short and closed.
Skin: Butter yellow, bright acid yellow green when unripe; smooth, waxy; very slight russet in eye and stem basins, occasionally spreading in patches and veins.
Flush: None.
Flesh: Mild sharp; rather mealy, yellowish.
Core: Axile, small, open, slightly distal; seeds few.
Juice: SG 1046; acidity 0.77%; tannin 0.14%.
Cider: When it was first tried at Long Ashton in 1926, Buttery Door cider was described as 'fair with an aromatic flavour but fermentation is too fast.'

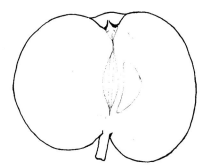

CADBURY
Mid Season Bittersweet
Synonyms: Royal Wildling, Pounset.

The name Cadbury is very old. This may be the original apple recorded by Billingsley in 1798 in his *Agricultural Survey of Somerset*, but even then it had the synonym of Pounset. Radcliffe-Cooke refers to it as an old bittersweet of great repute, but Hogg marks it down, declaring 'the cider quickly turns black after drawing'. Later, the work at Long Ashton demonstrated that cider can turn black through iron from the implements used during crushing and pressing, tainting the juice. Hogg's experience may have been through a fault of the cider-maker rather than any shortcomings of the variety. It was recorded under the name of Cadbury for the Bath and West Show in 1898 and fruit was often sent to Long Ashton in the early years. A few trees still exist in old trial orchards, both in Somerset and in Hereford where it is usually called Royal Wildling.

Cadbury trees grow upright and spreading like a pear tree and can be very long lived. It is recorded as being scab susceptible and is reputed to be a shy bearer, slow to come into cropping. 'When the Royal Wildling bears well', says a Herefordshire proverb, 'it is always a good cider year'. It must need a favourable season to perform at its best.

The variety flowers in early May. The apples are greenish-yellow with a very little flush, but often with considerable russeting, and they are ready in mid October.

Size: Medium to large, 55 to more than 60mm.
Shape: Flattened conical, sometimes tending to be waisted; rather ribbed.
Stem: Very short, a stub within a small, deep, golden russeted cavity.
Eye: Basin medium, narrow, deep, tending to crowned; sepals upright [royal], green.
Skin: Pale butter yellow; dry; covered with a distinctive network of russet, but sometimes without russet; lenticels corky, occasionally reddened.
Flush: A trace of pinkish-orange on some fruit.
Flesh: Mildly bittersweet; melting.
Core: Medium, axile, closed; tube conical; pronounced stylar column.
Juice: SG 1058; acidity 0.35%; tannin 0.22%.
Cider: Cadbury makes an excellent cider, consistently good, which may be placed alongside Dabinett in the bittersweet class. A rich, bitter cider with a full and pleasant taste and aroma.

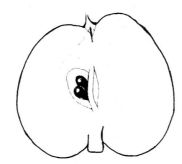

CAMELOT
Mid season Mild Bittersweet

This cider apple has been included in several lists as a culinary apple but its juice does have some astringency. It has been described variously as 'strongly resembling Newton Wonder' [Morgan] and 'A Somerset apple of the Annie Elizabeth type and shape . . . colour like Lane's Prince Albert but darker' [Taylor]. Fruits were exhibited at the RHS Exhibition in 1934.

Camelot flowers in May. Trees are vigorous and spreading with a poor centre leader. It is a partial tip-bearer.

This description of Somerset Camelot comes from fruit collected in the Mathew Clark cider apple collection at Shepton Mallet. The apples, which mature in mid-October, are usually medium sized, flattened and conical. The skin is yellow with a mottled and striped scarlet flush on one half but often they are without any red.

Size: Medium to large, 45-60mm.
Shape: Rather variable, cylindrical tending to conical in larger fruits, broad nose and base; angular with distinct ribs.
Stem: Thick, often fleshy, pubescent, projecting slightly or distinctly from a small, narrow but fairly deep basin.
Eye: Basin small but well defined, smooth, partly beaded, sometimes irregular with scab; sepals open, long, reflexed, sometimes green.
Skin: Pale green ripening to pale yellow; smooth, dry; scab susceptible; russet sometimes heavy in stem basin extending in patches and streaks over base; lenticels sometimes russet dots.
Flush: Usual, a trace to 40%; faint orange-brown diffuse and lightly striped or flecked pinkish-red.
Flesh: Mild bittersweet; chewy; yellowish.
Core: Medium, slightly proximal, abaxile, open, occasionally only 4 loculi; tube a large cone; stamens slightly proximal.
Juice: Mild bittersweet.
Cider: No cider-maker's notes found.

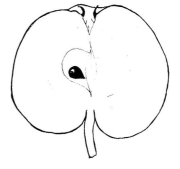

CAP OF LIBERTY
Mid-season Full Bittersharp
Synonyms: Red Soldiers, Bloody Soldier.

This is a well known and popular vintage quality apple which has always been highly recommended for cider making. It was first recorded at the Bath and West Show in 1895. It is a central Somerset variety originating in the Martock area where it was grown in moderate numbers in the nineteenth century. It still exists in some old orchards in south and central Somerset, and trial orchards planted before the 1920s. Cap of Liberty would have been planted in more recent bush orchards but for its propensity to disease, its poor tree habit and the small size of its fruit. Similar varieties include other Somerset sharps like Porter's Perfection and Lambrook Pippin.

The Cap of Liberty tree is a moderately vigorous, unwieldy fastigiate, multi-leader consisting of several long, unbranched, spreading limbs. It is a good, somewhat irregular cropper, preferring heavy, limestone derived soils. It is also rather susceptible to scab and apple sawfly. It flowers in late April or early May and the fruit is ready by mid October.

The fruit is a conical 'jersey' shape, rather cylindrical, with a non-existent eye basin and prominent brown lenticels on the pinkish-red flush. Its high acid content sets it apart as a 'balanced' juice, producing a rich, fruity and excellent cider.

Size: Small, 40-45mm.
Shape: Conical-cylindrical, rounded nose and base.
Stem: Slender, woody, projecting distinctly from a small, narrow cavity.
Eye: Basin slight or absent; eye beaded and puckered, slightly irregular; calyx usually open.
Skin: Yellow-green, dry, slightly rough; susceptible to scab which often disfigures the fruit; lenticels conspicuous as small, brown dots especially on flush, often associated with russet patches.
Flush: Always, 50% or more, diffuse pinkish red flecked with bright red.
Flesh: Sharp with light tannin, juicy, chewy and yellowish.
Core: Medium, open; tube medium, conical.
Juice: SG 1055; acidity 0.92%, tannin 0.30%.
Cider: Cap of Liberty makes a rich acid cider of excellent quality and body, with a good clean, fruity taste. Fermentation can be slow. Highly recommended as a vintage variety.

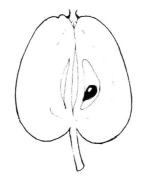

CHISEL JERSEY
Late Full Bittersweet
Synonyms: Sidestalk Jersey, Bitter Jersey or Jersey Chisel.

For 100 years the true Chisel Jersey, which originated in the Martock area, has been popular in Somerset, but it was not known outside its native county until the 1960s. Another variety, Sandford Jersey, which also originated in Somerset, was distributed in many West Midland orchards under the name Chisel Jersey. This is now referred to as Hereford Chisel Jersey. The true Somerset Chisel Jersey occurs frequently in bush orchards planted in the 1970's in Somerset and Dorset for Taunton Cider Company. It is losing its popularity through its habit of producing small cracked and severely russeted fruits in some seasons; a condition which could possibly be caused by virus infection, perhaps aggravated by insect damage or boron deficiency.

Bush trees of Chisel Jersey easily form a natural centre leader shape although they tend to get top heavy in middle age. They are fairly precocious and crop annually but flower late in May. Although a good pollinator, it is not self fertile and needs to be cross pollinated. Its half sister variety, Dabinett, which is one of the few varieties still flowering at the same time, is unsuitably incompatible, and fruit-set can be disappointing. Standard trees are large and semi-spreading. The leaves are neat and are shaped rather like cherry leaves, but are susceptible to scab.

The fruit which matures late, from November on, is a typical full bittersweet 'jersey', broad based and conical with a dark brownish-pink flush, striped red. Chisel Jersey can be difficult to distinguish from Sandford Jersey, but its offset stem is a useful character.

Size: Variable, medium, often small especially if russeted, 40-55mm.
Shape: Conical, broad nose and base; regularly rounded.
Stem: Projecting distinctly or slightly, fairly thick and woody, offset, strig frequently present; stem basin medium or small, shallow, usually flattened on one side.
Eye: Basin small, shallow and usually slightly puckered, corona sometimes present; calyx tightly closed, sepals touching, fairly long and reflexed, slightly pubescent but usually broken.
Skin: Greenish-yellow or yellow; smooth, slightly waxy; russet usual but variable, sometimes very severe and associated with cracks and distortion which severely reduced the size of the fruits, frequently the russet is patchy or as a fine net over the cheek of the fruit.

Flush: Always present to about 65%, diffuse and flecked brownish-pink or red.
Juice: SG 1059; acidity 0.22%; tannin 0.40%.
Cider: Chisel Jersey is reputed to make a strong, rich cider of high colour. It is a full bittersweet with astringent tannin, full bodied and of good quality, but it needs to be blended. Scott's Catalogue of 1893 is quotes it as 'perhaps the most esteemed bittersweet sort in the Somerset orchards . . . mixed with rich, sweet kinds ripening at the same time, it produces a cider of unequalled goodness.'

CHURCHILL
Late Medium Bittersweet

This variety was recorded in the 1960s as 'scattered trees in all the orchards' around Burrow Hill near Stembridge, Somerset. It was recommended at the time as a useful variety for more extensive propagation for Coates Cider to help meet the fruit requirements for the growing cider market. But it never did make a come-back. Last records of its propagation were in 1962, but some old trees were still cropping well on Burrow Hill in 1998.

It is a late maturing variety, not ready until the end of October or early November, and this may be the main reason for its lack of present popularity. Churchill flowers late mid season and the trees are large and spreading.

The fruit, with its dark crimson, heavy flush, looks like an unusually dark red Dabinett, to which it is probably closely related.

Size: Medium to large, 50 to more than 60mm.
Shape: Cylindrical with a flattened base; regular.
Stem: Short, thick and woody, within a shallow cavity, or projecting slightly.
Eye: Basin wide, shallow, slightly puckered and occasionally beaded; calyx usually open, sepals free, short with tips reflexed.
Skin: Pale yellow, smooth, dry; slight russet; lenticels sometimes corky dots but usually inconspicuous.
Flush: Always 30-60%, dull red, flecked carmine.
Flesh: Medium bittersweet, greenish, vascular strands showing a partial green line around the core when cut.
Core: Large loculi; the tube is a broad cone.
Juice: SG 1060; acidity 0.54%; tannin 0.15%.
Cider: No cider-maker's comments found at Long Ashton, but Coate's team in the 1960s deemed Churchill a good bittersweet for general use.

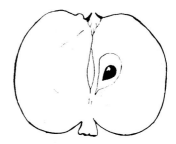

CIDER LADY'S FINGER
Early Mild Sharp

Lady's Finger is probably a generic name for varieties with fruits which are shaped longer than broad, elliptical and elongated. There are many Lady's Fingers from various places, notably Hereford. This West Country one has a little tannin in its juice and qualifies as a cider apple although it is probably more interesting as a curiosity.

The tree is compact and moderately vigorous, often drooping with fruit. It flowers in the second half of May, and crops biennially, the fruit maturing by early October.

The elongated fruit is a distinctive elliptical shape, plain yellow green with no flush and characteristic long stem. There is often a curious, fine ridge running across the cheek from eye to stem.

Size: Medium, 45-55mm.
Shape: Elliptical; rounded, regular.
Stem: Long, slender, woody, projecting distinctly; stem basin absent or very slight.
Eye: Basin absent or very slight, eye beaded or slightly irregular; calyx closed, sepals short, reflexed at tips.
Skin: Yellow to yellow-green, smooth and waxy; russet absent; lenticels with a pale surround.
Flush: Absent.
Flesh: Mild sharp with some tannin, rather non-descript; juicy, melting; greenish, browning rapidly when cut.
Core: Large, open, elliptical with few viable seeds; tube a shallow cup.
Juice: SG 1052, acidity 0.59%, tannin 0.12%.
Cider: This Lady's Finger makes a thin but pleasantly light, medium brisk cider with a fair aroma and flavour but lacking in body. It has moderate value for blending.

COAT JERSEY
Late Full Bittersweet
Synonym: possibly Twistbody Jersey.

This variety originated in the village of Coat, near Martock, before the twentieth century. Since the early 1970s it has been widely planted in bush orchards for Taunton Cider in Somerset and Dorset, where it crops heavily but biennially.

Coat Jersey trees are typically strong, upright and spreading. They produce sturdy growth that is sparsely spurred and often with much bare wood. The variety is also very prone to scab and in most years the fruit is badly marked and misshaped. It flowers mid season and is a good pollinator for other varieties.

The fruit on young trees is carried in clusters close to the main branches. It is a typical bittersweet 'jersey'. The apples are small, green and red striped, conical in shape and with a distinctive long stalk. It not ready until late October or early November.

Size: Small to medium, 40-55mm.
Shape: Conical or flattened conical; tending to ribbed.
Stem: Woody, projecting considerably from a deep basin.
Eye: Basin usually deep and puckered, often with ribbing extending from eye to cheek, calyx usually slightly open, sepals often reflexed at tip.
Skin: Greenish yellow; smooth; russet in stem basin only. Very scab susceptible.
Flush: Always present, up to30%, dark red striped.
Flesh: Sweet and astringent, white, sometimes greenish below the skin, woolly.
Core: Medium; tube variable, usually conical, often deep.
Juice: SG 1047; acidity 0.18%; tannin 0.27%.
Cider: Coat Jersey makes a bittersweet cider, full bodied and with a good character. Its aroma and flavour are good but it is too astringent alone and best blended.

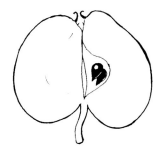

CONGRESBURY BEAUTY
Dual purpose
Synonym: Pople's Gutter Apple.

This attractive apple was raised in around 1880 by a Mr Pople, from a pip of an apple he picked up in a gutter outside Ushers Brewery in Trowbridge where he worked. He named it accordingly but modestly, Pople's Gutter Apple. In 1953, Mr Tom Day, a keen horticulturist, took some fruit from the tree in his garden in Congresbury to the Royal Horticultural Society Brains Trust. The experts recognised it as a seedling, so he told them that it was called Congresbury Beauty in his village because of its beautiful colour and form, and because he 'did not like the other name at all'. And so the new name stands. This information comes from Mrs Jean Day who keeps her father's memory alive through the Tom Day Memorial Cup, presented each year for the best fruit exhibit at the local Autumn Show which he founded.

Although there were many trees growing in Wrington Vale in the 1930s, the last known one died a few years ago. Fortunately, a few new trees were propagated just in time and Congresbury Beauty is thriving again in the Millennium orchard in the village.

As yet there are no fruit from which to get an accurate description, but it is known to be a striking red apple, somewhat like a Monarch in shape, perhaps like a rather deep, long-stemmed Newton Wonder. It is said to be a useful cooker and well worth growing for its appearance. Mr T. Usher of Trowbridge can be quoted as having said 'when there is a well covered tree of ripe fruit, it is one of the most striking objects in the garden'. Its season is November to December.

Juice: SG 1050; acidity 0.90%; tannin 0.27%.
Cider: Long Ashton recorded in the early 1900s that Pople's Gutter Apple made a sweet cider of marked acidity and rather harsh flavour, as to be expected from a dual purpose fruit which would normally be blended with other varieties.

COURT DE WICK
Mid season Dessert
Synonyms: Court of Wyck, Fry's Pippin, Golden Drop, Woods Huntingdon etc.

This old apple is said to have originated at Court of Wick in Claverham, raised from a pip of Golden Pippin and 'may be considered a beautiful variety of that fruit', to quote Billingsley's *Survey of Somersetshire*. 'The favourite apple, both as a table and cider fruit . . . In shape, colour and flavour, it has not its superior'. It was introduced to commerce around 1790 by Mr Wood, nurseryman of Huntingdon and that is how one of its synonyms arose.

Mature standard trees are medium sized, healthy, hardy and abundant bearers. Hogg describes Court of Wick as one of the best and most valuable dessert apples, both as regards the hardiness of the tree and the fruit, which is rich and delicious in flavour. It would seem that it should be more widely grown nowadays.

The apples, which mature in October and are said to keep until March, are rounded, and russeted over a rich orange flush. The wide open eye is a noticeable character.

Size: Medium, 50mm.
Shape: Rounded, cylindrical tending to ovate; regular.
Stem: Short, slender in a shallow, russeted cavity.
Eye: Basin wide, shallow and even; calyx open, sepals long, reflexed.
Skin: Pale yellow, covered with fine russeted lenticels.
Flush: Usually less than 30%, bright orange, sometimes red nearest the sun.
Flesh: Sub-acid; crisp, yellow, juicy and highly flavoured.
Core: Axile; tube funnel shaped; stamens median.
Juice: SG 1079; acidity 0.29%; tannin 0.10%.
        From a fruit sample sent to Long Ashton by Mr Shatford of Wick Court in 1908.

Ashton Bitter

Ashton Brown Jersey

Backwell Red

Bell

Broadleaf Jersey

Brown's Apple

Brown Snout

Bulmer's Norman

Burrow Hill Early

Buttery Door

Cadbury

Camelot

Cap of Liberty

Chisel Jersey

Churchill

Cider Lady's Finger

Coat Jersey

Court de Wick

Court Royal

Crimson King

Dabinett

Dove

Dunkerton's Late

Early Red Jersey

Ellis Bitter

Fair Maid of Taunton

Fillbarrel

Gin

Hangdown

Harry Master's Jersey

Hoary Morning

Honeystring

Improved Dove

Improved Hangdown

Improved Kingston Black

Improved Lambrook Pippin

Improved Woodbine

King's Favourite

Kingston Black

Lambrook Pippin

Langworthy

Le Bret

Long Tom

Major

Michelin

Morgan Sweet

Neverblight

Norton Bitters

Pennard Bitter

Pig's Snout

Poor Man's Profit

Porter's Perfection

Red Jersey

Red Worthy

Royal Jersey

Royal Somerset

Sharpshooter

Sheep's Nose

Shoreditch White

Silver Cup

Slack-ma-Girdle

Somerset

Somerset Redstreak

Sops in Wine

Stable Jersey

Stembridge Clusters

Stembridge Jersey

Stoke Red

Stubbard

Sweet Coppin

Sweet Alford

Sweet Pethyre

Taylor's Sweet

Ten Commandments

Tommy Rodford

Tom Putt

Tom Putt, Red

Tremlett's Bitter

Vallis Apple, Black

Vallis Apple, Red

Wear and Tear

White Close Pippin

White Jersey

Woodbine

Yarlington Mill

Yellow Redstreak

A familiar sight at any cider mill in the autumn, fruit waiting to be pressed in the late 1950s .

These cider apple varieties were selected for the 'new' orchards of the 1970s, and now form the basis of many of the Somerset bush orchard plantings. (Left to right): Harry Masters' Jersey, Brown's Apple, Yarlington Mill, Chisel Jersey, Michelin, Dabinett and Coat Jersey.

Cider apples in a Somerset bush orchard beginning to size up and colour in midsummer.

A traditional Somerset standard orchard with massive Bulmers Norman trees in full bloom.

Modern bush orchards are both beautiful and a haven for wildlife. Somerset redstreak, Tremletts Bitter and Michelin in full bloom.

COURT ROYAL
Late Pure Sweet
Synonyms: Pound, Pound Apple, Improved Pound, Sweet Blenheim.

Mature trees are found throughout Somerset and East Devon. At the beginning of the twentieth century Court Royal was used as a dessert apple in many industrial areas and followed Morgan Sweet in to the markets. It no longer has any dessert appeal and is just used for cider making. Few new trees are planted except as replacements in old orchards. Early records of this variety at the Cider Institute come from fruit sent in from Court Barton, Newton St Cyres in Devon, and this may be where it was named, although bearing one of the synonyms in other locations. It gets it 'royal' epithet from its distinctive calyx; the eye is always open and the sepals are long, upright and free, forming a small crown on the top of the fruit. In Somerset it is usually called Pound Apple or Sweet Blenheim.

Mature trees are large, vigorous and spreading. Court Royal is a triploid and its vigour was often exploited as a stem builder for top-working with other weaker varieties. The grafts frequently re-grow in old trees to produce a head of Court Royal intermingled with the original variety. Sometimes its exuberance will overtake the weaker variety altogether. Young trees are slow to bear but settle down to crop well, although this variety is rather prone to brown rot and scab.

The fruit bears a distinct similarity to a well coloured Bramley's Seedling in everything else but taste; large and green with an orange flush and distinctive upright sepals. It is not ready for harvest until early November but may start falling in October and begin to rot.

Size:	Usually large, usually more than 60mm.
Shape:	Flattened spherical, sometimes oblate; sometimes irregular.
Stem:	Thick and fleshy, within a variable shallow to deep basin.
Eye:	Basin usually very deep, smooth and sometimes irregular; calyx usually open, sepals upright, fairly long, free, green at the base, pubescent.
Skin:	Yellow or greenish-yellow, smooth with very little wax; sometimes slight russet in the stem basin; lenticels usually not conspicuous, but sometimes large and irregular in the stem basin where they may be surrounded by a white or dark green patch.
Flush:	Always present, about 60%, orange diffuse flush, flecked and occasionally slightly striped with dark red.
Flesh:	Pure sweet; white or slightly greenish, slightly crisp.
Core:	Median, axile, loculi sometimes open; tube usually conical and shallow, rarely extending to a funnel.
Juice:	SG 1050; acidity 0.21%; tannin 0.11%.
Cider:	Court Royal ferments quickly to a pure sweet cider.

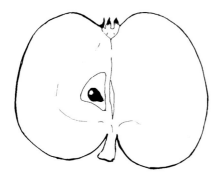

CRIMSON KING
Late Sharp

Synonyms: John Toucher's, Jackson's, Bewley Down Pippin.

This variety was first propagated by Mr John Toucher of Bewley Down, Chardstock, hence its synonyms, but was later named Crimson King when it was adopted by the nursery trade. It occurs as mature trees in western Somerset and adjacent parts of Devon, and in orchards planted in the 1950s. It is sometimes used as a replacement in old orchards that have been kept gapped up, but it has not been chosen recently for use in bush orchards because of its vigour.

Crimson King flowers mid season but it is a triploid and therefore a poor pollinator. It is vigorous and makes a large, spreading tree with much bare, unspurred wood when young, but it is reputed to crop generously and fairly annually as it matures.

The fruit is usually quite large, resembling a Bramley, from which it is distinguished by its dark red striped flush and deep, open eye. It also matures much later than Bramley, not being ready until mid November. Juice from this variety is medium sharp and makes a light and fruity cider of fair quality.

Size:	Medium or large, 55 to more than 60mm.
Shape:	Variable, usually conical, rarely cylindrical, round or oblate; irregular.
Stem:	Stout, fleshy or woody, rarely bulging at junction with fruit or spur, projecting very slightly or level with the base; stem basin variable, small but can be deep or shallow.
Eye:	Basin fairly wide, usually deep, often irregular and slightly ribbed; calyx open, sepals long if not broken, reflexed and free.
Skin:	Greenish-yellow; smooth, slightly waxy; russet usual, spreading over cheek, usually in streaks, often rough and scaly in stem basin. Scab susceptible.
Flush:	Usually 30-65%, mainly diffuse, with some crimson flecking and striping.
Flesh:	Sharp with no astringency; white or greenish, sometimes reddened below skin.
Core:	Median or slightly proximal, axile, loculi small, sometimes open; tube wide, conical.
Juice:	SG 1044; acidity 0.60%; tannin 0.13%.
Cider:	In a good year Crimson King cider can be good alone without blending. It is medium sharp, light and fruity and usually of above average quality. Fermentation can be rather rapid and the sugar content is often low.

DABINETT
Late Full Bittersweet

Dabinett comes from mid Somerset. It was found as a 'gribble', a self-sown seedling, probably a seedling of Chisel Jersey, in a hedge in Middle Lambrook by Mr William Dabinett, a local Somerset man. It was propagated extensively by Charles Porter, nurseryman of East Lambrook, where there are still some fine trees. It is common in standard and bush orchards throughout all the cider growing counties because of its well justified reputation for good and regular crops. It holds top place for the most popular and highly esteemed variety for current bush planting.

Dabinett trees are usually small with a neat rounded head. Their vigour is only moderate and the final tree size depends on the soil type and conditions. Bush trees are very susceptible to soil potash deficiency. Young trees are moderately vigorous with plenty of lateral branches at good angles, but leader growth is weak and may quickly loose dominance. Spurring is moderately good and cropping usually heavy and regular. Older standard trees may be short lived due to a sensitivity to virus infection. Characteristically Dabinett will produce secondary blossom which may appear at any time of the year, even in the autumn, but their normal flowering period is late mid season. The variety has become slightly susceptible to both mildew and scab in bush orchards, although it seems fairly resistant in old farm orchards.

The fruit, which matures in early November, is a typical 'jersey' type of cider apple, medium sized, rounded, conical and heavy, with a dark red striped flush. The juice is sweet with a soft, full astringency and the cider it makes is usually high quality and well balanced.

Size:	Medium, sometimes small, 40-55mm.
Shape:	Flattened conical, sometimes round; regular; very occasionally fruits are twinned.
Stem:	Thin and woody, projecting slightly, sometimes distinctly from a small basin, narrow at the base, sometimes shallow, particularly in king fruits.
Eye:	Basin usually slight and shallow, slightly puckered or smooth; calyx tightly closed, sometimes slightly open, sepals short.
Skin:	Yellow or greenish yellow; smooth and waxy; russet slight in stem basin, spreading to cheek; lenticels not usually apparent but sometimes large, corky and conspicuous.

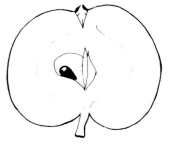

Flush:	Always, present, usually more than 65%, flecked and slightly striped pinkish-red with extensive diffuse background.
Flesh:	Sweet and astringent; greenish or white; slightly crisp.
Core:	Median, abaxile sometimes axile with loculi open; tube conical, stamens distal.
Juice:	SG 1057, acidity 0.18%; tannin 0.29%.
Cider:	Dabinett cider is usually high quality and well balanced, full bittersweet but with a soft astringency and full bodied. It is suitable for blending or using alone as an excellent single variety cider for the connoisseur.

DOVE
Late Medium Bittersweet
Synonym: Pennard Dove.

Dove is probably a very old variety which was first recorded by Lloyd for the Bath and West Show in 1899. It is likely to have originated in Glastonbury, at the once famous nurseries on the side of the Tor. It is frequently found in old orchards in that area of Somerset where is still known as Pennard Dove. It was very popular at one time because of its late flowering habit which suited the frost susceptible, low lying orchards of that area, but has become more and more prone to scab and has consequently lost its popularity. The traditional good qualities of this variety are reflected in the number of more recent introductions which have been named after it, for example Improved Dove, Late Dove and Stone Dove. Small numbers of Dove were included in a few orchards planted for Taunton Cider Company in the early 1970s.

Dove itself forms a distinctive tree. It is small with dense, well spurred, drooping branches and rough, greyish foliage. Many old trees died through heavy virus infection, and surviving examples of Dove usually show symptoms of debility and carry some dead wood. The fruit is also very susceptible to scab. As a bush tree it is small and densely branched. It is precocious and cropping can be regular and heavy but its performance is variable with district and disease. Dove flowers in late May, is diploid and a good pollinator.

The fruits are a typical 'jersey' shape, small conical, rather waisted with a broad base. They become extremely waxy when they are really mature, which is not before the first week of November. The eye of the fruit is tightly closed with long sepals often overlapping. When cut through the flesh is white round the outside but green near the core; displaying a distinct line of prominent green vascular strands.

Size:	Small to medium, 40-50mm.
Shape:	Waisted, conical, rarely conico-cylindrical, base broad.
Stem:	Thick, usually woody, within the cavity or level with the base, rarely projecting slightly; stem basin variable, medium, usually shallow, sometimes deep.
Eye:	Basin usually medium and shallow, sometimes slight, rarely deep, puckered, frequently ribbed, often slightly beaded; calyx tightly closed, sepals touching, often overlapping, fairly long, reflexed at tip, usually broken.
Skin:	Green or yellowish-green; smooth and very waxy; russet confined to stem basin, heavy and scaly, occasionally spreading to cheek; lenticels inconspicuous except on bruises, occasionally dark green. Scab susceptible.
Flush:	Always present but variable, usually 30-65%, lightly flecked and slightly

striped, sometimes a little diffuse, rarely striped only, red.

Flesh: Sweet, usually with some astringency, pleasant flavour; white, yellowish or greenish-white, but white inside a circle of prominent green vascular strands; slightly woolly and juicy.

Core: Median, axile, loculi closed or slightly open; seeds round and numerous; tube conical.

Juice: SG 1049; acidity 0.22%; tannin 0.31%.

Cider: Dove cider is mild bittersweet and only rather average quality but with good body, soft tannin and a pleasant flavour. Sugar content is often below average and fermentation slow.

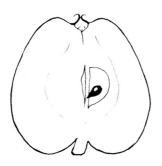

DUNKERTON'S LATE
Late Sweet
Synonym: Dunkerton's Sweet.

This apple was raised by Mr Dunkerton, of Baltonsborough, near Glastonbury in the 1940s, probably from a seedling saved from pomace. It has been adopted in a limited way for traditional orchards, especially its home area, and can be found growing and cropping well as youngish or middle aged standard trees.

Dunkerton's Late flowers late mid-season. Although fairly vigorous, it forms a naturally good shape and is well spurred. It is robust and fairly disease resistant with some potential as a late harvesting variety, but it has never become popular for bush orchards because of its late ripening season.

Dunkerton's Late is a broad shouldered cylinder shaped apple, yellow with an orange flush, but it is often harvested too early when it its still green and its flush is mauvish. It is distinguished by its lateness, it is not really ready until late November, and the wide open eye surrounded by short, free sepals.

Size: Medium, 45-55mm.

Shape: Cylindrical tending towards conical, broad nose and broad rounded base; rounded or slightly oval in section.

Stem: Often a woody stub within the cavity or projecting slightly; stem basin medium, narrow, deep.

Eye: Basin medium, broad and shallow, smooth or slightly bumpy, tending to crowned; calyx wide open, sepals free, short, green.

Skin: Cold pea green but primrose yellow when ripe; smooth and dry; russet usually confined to stem cavity, golden; lenticels conspicuous pale surround, milky on unripe fruits.

Flush: Always present, variable, up to 70%; diffuse or speckled pinkish-mauve to brownish-red.

Flesh: Sweet; very firm, chewy; pale yellow or greenish with green vascular strands.

Core: Rather small, median, closed; seeds numerous; tube a broad cone, occasionally extending to a funnel.

Juice: SG 1047; acidity 0.22%, tannin 0.09%.

Cider: A sweet, light and fruity cider.

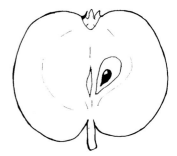

EARLY RED JERSEY
Early Bittersweet
Synonyms: Royal Jersey II, Port Wine.

Early Red Jersey is one of a group of similar looking bittersweet apples; Royal Jersey, Red Jersey and many seedlings, from which it is distinguished with difficulty by its earlier maturity. It is ready in early October, some three weeks before the others. This variety probably originated in the Glastonbury to Shepton Mallet area, where it is still found. Although it was included in Professor A.T.B. Barker's list of recommended varieties under the name Royal Jersey II, it has never been adopted for bush orchards.

Early Red Jersey forms a fair sized tree in a loose umbrella shape, and cropping is said to be good and growth hardy. It flowers in early May, again well before the others. It is sometimes described as a 'good all round sort', but like the other Jerseys, it is rather scab prone.

The fruits are a typical 'Jersey' shape, conical with a rather flattened nose and broad base. When ripe, they are well covered with a dark red flush, streaked and flecked with crimson and often quite russeted. Its synonym Port Wine is a tribute to its excellent, rich cider.

Size: Medium, 45-55 mm.
Shape: Conical, base broad, rounded, nose flattened; slightly oval in section.
Stem: Short, usually within a small, fairly deep cavity.
Eye: Basin slight, narrow, shallow; calyx open, sepals long, reflexed.
Skin: Green, smooth, dry; streaky russet spreading from eye; scab susceptible.
Flush: Always, 30-70%, dark red striped and flecked crimson.
Flesh: Mild bittersweet; greenish, juicy, chewy.
Core: Median, closed, tube conical.
Juice: SG 1050; acidity 0.22%; tannin 0.26%.
Cider: Although the fermentation is reported to be slow and sometimes irregular, the juice is medium bittersweet and the sugar content is frequently unusually high, so the resulting cider is always rich and full-bodied.

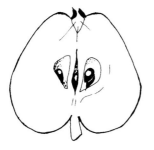

ELLIS BITTER
Early Bittersweet

Ellis Bitter is a Devon variety which was distributed outside the county in some of the Long Ashton trial orchards planted in the 1930s. It is enjoying recent popularity as an early maturing bittersweet, growing and cropping with some success in a number of new bush orchards planted during the late 1990s.

Mature standard trees are frequently large with a spreading habit. Young bush trees are fast growing and rather upright but respond to training to produce a good centre leader. Cropping is fairly regular and the fruit is heavy. It is slightly prone to scab but not mildew. Flowering time is mid May.

Ellis Bitter apples are large and bold, covered in a heavily flecked flush which sometimes has a bluish tinge. They do not keep well and are often attacked by birds attracted to their bright shiny skin, which makes them rot even more quickly. It is one of the earliest to mature in modern bush orchards, ready late September.

Size: Large, rarely medium, usually more than 60mm.
Shape: Conical, base flat, nose pointed; sometimes tending to ribbed.
Stem: Thick, often slightly off-set, often with a bulge at spur end; level with the base or projecting slightly from a narrow, deep basin.
Eye: Basin well defined, often deep and irregular; calyx slightly open, sepals short, often green and pubescent.
Skin: Yellow to greenish-yellow; smooth, waxy; russet slight; slight scab.
Flush: Always present, virtually complete; diffuse background sometimes absent, always heavily flecked and striped dark red; sometimes with a purplish tinge.
Flesh: Sweet and astringent; white; crisp and juicy.

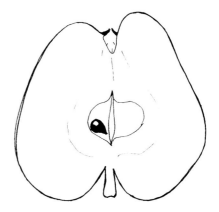

Core: Slightly proximal, irregular, open, sometimes only 4 loculi.
Juice: SG 1053; acidity 0.20%; tannin 0.24%.
Cider: A good quality medium bittersweet with soft, astringent tannin, rather thin on its own and better blended.

FAIR MAID OF TAUNTON
Mid Season Mild Sharp
Synonyms: Moonshines or Moonlight, Greasy Butcher.

This variety is described by Hogg in the early nineteenth century as a dessert apple, but not of the first quality. It was recorded in the National Apple Register in 1831. Although it was only infrequently sent in for cider making trials, it made an agreeable though rather characterless cider. Its juice is quite high in acid and described as rather 'Devon type', that is a flat, mild sharp. Although it probably hails from Taunton or that area, it is still often found in orchards around Glastonbury where it is usually called Moonshines. It is said to have got the name because its pale yellow apples shine in the moonlight and can still be seen to be picked up after dark!

Trees are large, tall and spreading. Flowering time is early May. It is rather scab susceptible.

The fruit is large, rounded and conspicuously butter yellow when ripe come mid to late October.

Size: Large to medium, 40-55mm.
Shape: Oblate or conical; rounded, ribbed on body, sometimes rather irregular.
Stem: Short, thick and fleshy, occasionally strigged, projecting distinctly from a small, shallow basin.
Eye: Basin shallow, often broad, slightly irregular and beaded; calyx often open, sepals broad, flat, reflexed.
Skin: Pale green or whitish, turning butter yellow; smooth, dry, greasy when ripe; russet sometimes heavy in stem cavity and spreading netted over the cheek; lenticels sometimes corky with a pale surround on immature fruit, often with a red or brown dot when ripe.
Flush: Slight hint of red on sunny side; to about 30%, diffuse, speckled or flecked pink or pinkish orange.
Flesh: Sharp with some astringency; white or yellowish, tender, juicy, chewy.
Core: Median, open; tube conical, stamens slightly proximal.
Juice: SG 1047; acidity 0.55%; tannin 0.19%.
Cider: Moderately sweet with some acidity, Fair Maid of Taunton makes a cider with a fairly agreeable aroma and flavour, but lacking in character.

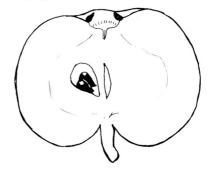

FILLBARREL
Late Mid Season Bittersweet

Most old records come from the Woolston, Sutton Montis, Wincanton area of south-east Somerset where a few old trees can still be found. Fillbarrel is probably a late nineteenth century apple. It was included in the Long Ashton trial orchards planted in 1957, and subsequently in a few orchards planted for Taunton Cider in 1970s.

Mature trees are vigorous, spreading and densely branched. Young trees can be poorly spurred with much bare wood. Although it can crop heavily, Fillbarrel is biennial and fills the barrels only every other year. It is very early flowering, at the end of April or early May, and unlike most cider apples, occasionally gets caught by late frosts. If the flowers are damaged the crop can be lost.

The attractive fruit is a neat cylindrical shape, dark red flushed and covered with a distinctive network of golden russet. It is mature from mid to late October and is said to make a good, medium cider.

Size: Medium, 45-55mm, can be very small with heavy crops.
Shape: Cylindrical; usually rounded sometimes lopsided.
Stem: A thick stub within the small, tight, deep stem cavity.
Eye: Basin large, broad and deep, smooth; calyx open, sepals short, free in an upright crown.
Skin: Yellow green; rough and dry; russet heavy round eye basin, spreading all over as a golden network; lenticels conspicuous, russeted.
Flush: Always 30-65%, diffuse scarlet flush with crimson flecks and some stripes.
Flesh: Mild bittersweet; yellowish, crisp, juicy, chewy.
Core: Often small with few seeds; tube large, a broad cone.
Juice: SG 1062; acidity 0.25%; tannin 0.30%.
Cider: Fillbarrel makes a good medium cider, full bodied and with well marked astringency.

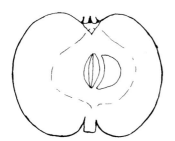

GIN
Early Sharp
Synonym: Gatcombe.

The apples shown at the Bath and West Exhibition in 1893 were noted to come from Butleigh, and Gin is still fairly frequently found in the area around Glastonbury. It picked up its synonym Gatcombe when it was sent in to the Cider Institute for cider making trials in 1910 as an unknown cider apple from Gatcombe Farm, Long Ashton. But the name Gin suits it well since the juice is clean and fresh flavoured and the cider it makes is sweet with a fruity aroma. Having been pronounced useful, it was then distributed over the other counties in the earliest trial orchards planted pre 1920.

Mature trees are medium sized, compact with a dense, round head. Crops are regular and heavy. Young bush trees tend to be upright, spreading and open. It flowers late in May.

Gin fruit is conical and yellow with a large, ribbed eye and sometimes a brilliant patch of flush. It matures and drops early in October but because the skin is rather delicate, the fruit does not keep well on the ground.

Size: Medium, but can be fairly large, 45-60mm.
Shape: Flattened conical, sometimes tending to cylindrical with a broad nose and narrow rounded base; ribbed and often irregular.
Stem: Woody, sometimes strigged, within or projecting slightly from a small, tight cavity; stem basin absent in off-year king fruits.
Eye: Basin medium, well defined, often slightly puckered or crowned, distinctly ribbed; calyx open, sepals upright, short, green at base.
Skin: Pale soft yellow; smooth, slightly waxy; scab susceptible; russet usually slight but occasionally heavy in the stem basin and spreading in a network over cheek; lenticels small green or red dots.
Flush: Occasionally present, usually less than one third; thin orange or pink.
Flesh: Mild sharp with some mild astringency, clear fresh flavour; white or greenish-white, melting texture.
Core: Large, sometimes open; tube a broad cone or funnel, often open part way to core.
Juice: SG 1060; acidity 0.20%; tannin 0.22%.
Cider: Very pleasant sweet, full bodied, with medium acidity. Flavour and aroma fruity and good. Fermentation slow to medium. Gin cider is very useful alone or blended.

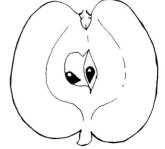

HANGDOWN
Bittersweet
Synonyms: Horners, Hangydown, Pocket Apple [in Devon].

A Hangdown tree is easily identified by its habit. It is compact, usually fairly small sized, with many twiggy branches which droop when heavy with fruit. Once highly recommended for cider making, Hangdown is widely distributed throughout Somerset and North Devon, where it is often called Pocket Apple. It also occurs in a few old trials orchards in other counties but is no longer in favour because of the small size of its fruit. There are several closely related varieties going under the name of Hangdown, all with the same drooping habit and similar fruit. Many of them are seedlings, or so-called Improved Hangdowns. The true Hangdown is said to have originated in the Glastonbury area where it still occurs quite frequently.

Hangdown crops well and regularly on light soils but lacks vigour on heavy land. It is quite scab susceptible and flowers rather late in May.

The small green fruits which usually hang in clusters, are round with long, thin stems. Usually there is a patch of thin red or pinkish-orange flush on the cheeks. The cores are tightly stuffed full of seeds. They are usually ready to drop by late October.

Size: Small, less than 40-45mm.
Shape: Rounded or slightly cylindrical with a narrow rounded base.
Stem: Thin and woody, sometimes swelling slightly at the junction with the fruit, projecting distinctly or considerably from a small, narrow, deep basin.
Eye: Basin medium, large for the size of the fruit, deep, usually puckered and slightly beaded, ribbed; calyx closed or slightly open, sepals touching, reflexed at the tips, sometimes green at the base.
Skin: Yellow or greenish-yellow; smooth and slightly waxy; russet usually confined to stem basin, sometimes streaky or a network over part of the cheek; lenticels usually inconspicuous but sometimes large and corky or red on the flush.
Flush: Usual, often less than 30%, rarely up to 60%; diffuse, pinkish-orange or red.
Flesh: Sweet and usually slightly astringent; yellowish-white; very soft.
Core: Median, axile, frequently less than 5 loculi, loculi small; seeds numerous and round; tube variable, a fairly deep cone or funnel.
Juice: SG 1056; acidity 0.20%; tannin 0.28%.
Cider: Hangdown is only mildly bittersweet and makes average quality cider.

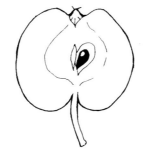

HARRY MASTERS' JERSEY
Late Mid-season, Bittersweet
Synonym: Port Wine.

A typical Somerset 'jersey' apple both in its shape and astringency, Harry Masters' Jersey is said to be named after the man who raised both it and Yarlington Mill, in the village of that name in South Somerset. Mr Masters is reputed to have been the miller at Yarlington Mill, but he has also been described as a 'nurseryman of Woolston around 1850.' Both Harry Masters' Jersey and Yarlington Mill are probably seedlings with the same parentage. Both have been widely planted and are still very successful in modern bush cider orchards. Harry Masters' was included in the earliest trial orchards planted before 1920.

A Harry Masters' tree is medium sized with a compact head. The bark of young trees has distinct lenticels which make it easy to distinguish from other varieties during the dormant season. As a bush tree its crops are not heavy but are fairly regular. Crops from traditional orchards are biennial but good. Harry Masters' flowers late mid-season just before Chisel Jersey, but its blossom overlaps sufficiently to make it a good pollinator for that variety.

Harry Masters' Jersey fruit is often very large in young bush trees, and can be prone to water core. It is typical conical 'jersey' shape with a pointed nose, flushed dark red and coated with a fine, distinctive bluish, waxy bloom. It is quite a late apple, ready late October to early November.

Size: Medium, often large on young trees, 45-55mm.
Shape: Conical with a flattened base and a pointed nose tending to a snout.
Stem: Projecting slightly but often level with the base; basin medium.
Eye: Basin smallish, shallow, puckered, often ribbed; calyx usually closed or slightly open, sepals touching, short, green at base.
Skin: Greenish-yellow; smooth, covered when ripe with a bluish, waxy bloom; russet confined to stem basin or spreading slightly; lenticels often conspicuous, large, corky, surrounded by patch of russet.
Flush: More than 65%, diffuse, flecked and slightly striped dark red.
Flesh: Sweet and astringent; white, sometimes reddened below skin; hard and dry.
Core: Median, axile, loculi open; seeds numerous; tube conical; stamens median.
Juice: SG 1056; acidity 0.20%; tannin 0.32%.
Cider: Medium to full bittersweet, Harry Masters' Jersey has soft astringent tannin and makes a very good quality cider.

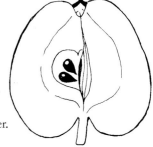

HOARY MORNING
Sharp dual purpose
Synonyms: Variously called Bachelor's Glory, Lambrook Seedling, Hoary Jack; possibly also Red Streaked Rawlings, Sam Rawlings or Dainty Apple.

Recorded as Sam Rawlings in 1819 this variety was described later as an 'old Somersetshire apple, frequently seen in the western counties.' Lindley, 1829 described it as 'Hoary Morning . . . this very handsome and useful apple'. In 1884 Hogg somewhat puzzlingly described it as 'A beautiful and very good culinary apple of second rate quality.' Very probably, Hoary Morning came from Porter's nursery in Lambrook, mid Somerset from where it was distributed as a dual purpose apple, at first called Lambrook Seedling.

Hoary Morning trees are only moderately vigorous. Flowering is mid season.

The fruits are round and flat, strongly striped bright red and green, and with a distinctive white bloom overall which is especially pretty when they are still fresh and young. The flesh is crisp and dry, and the juice has plenty of acidity.

It is reported to cook well and would probably give a fresh sharpness to a bittersweet Somerset farm cider. It matures in early October but keeps well until January.

Size: Medium, 50 to more than 60mm.
Shape: Oblate or flattened conical; rather ribbed on the body, lopsided or angular.
Stem: Short, green, sometimes strigged, within a small, fairly deep basin.
Eye: Basin small, rather bumpy or ribbed; calyx more or less closed, sepals reflexed.
Skin: Pale green - yellowish; smooth, dry, dull, a conspicuous white bloom overall; some russet in stem basin.
Flush: Always present, 30-60%; pale red, strongly striped on sunny side except nose end; bright red and dull crimson.
Flesh: Sharp, strongly acidic; white sometimes tinged red; crisp.
Core: Axile, usually closed; tube a funnel.
Juice: SG 1043; acidity 0.50-60%; tannin 0.18%.
Cider: No cider-makers notes found. Hoary Morning would blend well with bittersweet varieties.

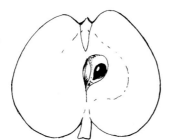

HONEYSTRING
Late sweet

First mention of this variety was in the Bath and West Special Exhibition in 1895 when a sample was sent from Butleigh. Later records came from Shepton Mallet and its first cider trial at Long Ashton raised the comment, 'A good sweet cider'. Honeystring trees can still be found in old orchards around West Bradley, Pilton and Glastonbury.

Honeystring makes a smallish, compact, trouble-free tree. It flowers early and crops are regular and good.

The fruit is broadly conical, a very pale green apple with a bumpy, knobbed eye and only a very short stub for a stem. Maturing mid to late October.

Size: Fairly large, 55-60mm.
Shape: Flattened conical, base broad; usually rounded but tending to be angular.
Stem: Usually very short, occasionally just a short stub within cavity; stem basin large, broad, deep.
Eye: Basin medium, bumpy; calyx more or less closed.
Skin: Very pale green; smooth and waxy; russet usually confined to stem basin; lenticels small green dots, occasionally reddened.
Flush: Frequent, usually less than 30%, slightly speckled or diffuse, brownish-orange.
Flesh: Sweet; juicy, melting and chewy, white.
Core: Large, slightly proximal; tube a deep cone often open to the core.
Juice: SG 1052; acidity 0.24%; tannin 0.10%.
Cider: The first cider made at Long Ashton in the 1930s was described as, 'a good sweet cider, crisp and dry.'

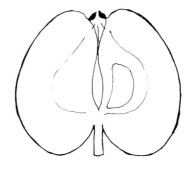

IMPROVED DOVE
Mid Season Mild Bittersweet

This is one of the many 'improvements' on the popular Somerset variety Dove or Pennard Dove. Although having excellent vintage qualities, the true Dove lost its resistance to scab, was predisposed to virus infection and consequently fell out of favour. Improved Dove, Stone Dove, Dove Seedling, Late Dove and others, are more recent introductions, probably all seedlings of the true Dove coming, as many of them did, from the Glastonbury area in the early part of the century. Improved Dove was originally resistant to scab and is the only one to have survived in significant numbers in Somerset.

Improved Dove quickly makes a strong tree, upright but spreading with crop and with a good, dominant centre leader. Although lateral branches are a bit sparse in young trees, spurring is free. It is a partial tip bearer, so cropping is regular at first but often becomes biennial. This variety may also have become prone to scab by now, but perhaps not so much as the original Dove. It flowers late, from mid May to the end of the month.

The fruit is tall, broadly conical, yellow striped and very similar to Dove itself but usually larger and slightly later, maturing mid October to early November.

Size:	Medium, 45-55mm.
Shape:	Conical, elongated sometimes with a nose; fairly regular or slightly elliptical in section.
Stem:	Woody or sometimes fleshy, level with base or projecting slightly from a small, conical basin, stem basin often appearing deeper in section.
Eye:	Basin small, slightly puckered and ribbed tending to shoulders; calyx tightly closed, sepals fairly long and overlapping.
Skin:	Green or yellow green; smooth, waxy; scab susceptible; russet confined to stem basin, rarely spreading over cheek; lenticels usually inconspicuous, sometimes with a light surround.
Flush:	Usually 30-70%, lightly flecked and striped, dark red, over brownish-orange diffuse.
Flesh:	Mild bittersweet; soft, juicy; greenish white, browning rapidly; vascular strands green, showing an incomplete green line in section.
Core:	Median, open with many seeds; tube a fairly deep cone.
Juice:	SG 1050, acidity 0.17%, tannin 0.38%.
Cider:	No cider-maker's notes found. Likely to be a useful bittersweet for blending or sufficiently mild to be palatable on its own as a single variety cider.

IMPROVED HANGDOWN
Mid Season Bittersweet
Synonyms: Improved Horners, Osier.

Most records of fruit sent to Long Ashton came from the Glastonbury to Wedmore area in the early 1900s, when the variety was first recorded as Improved Hangdown or Horners. It was exhibited at the RHS show in 1934 but has never been widely propagated. It was collected from the Whetton's Museum orchard in 1974 and subsequently sent to the National Fruit Trials collection at Brogdale, by then named Osier.

The tree is rather weak and weeping like the true Hangdown. Flowering time is mid May. The apples which are ready for harvesting by the end of October, are pale green with a trace of pink on the sunny side, conical and crowned. The distinctive sepals are broad, green and leafy.

Size:	Medium to large, 45-60mm.
Shape:	Cylindrical, broad nose and base; rounded tending to ribbed.
Stem:	Long, thin, woody, projecting slightly or distinctly from a medium, deep basin; stem short, basin slight in king fruit.
Eye:	Basin medium, narrow, deep, crowned and furrowed, sometimes beaded; sepals partially open, long, green and leafy.
Skin:	Pale yellow-green; smooth, dry becoming waxy; scab susceptible; lenticels sometimes small red dots on flush only.
Flush:	Frequently a trace to 30% on the sunny side, pink or brownish orange diffuse.
Flesh:	Sweet with mild astringency; pleasant flavour, chewy, greenish.
Core:	Medium, median, axile, open, often only 4 loculi present; tube a broad deep cone; stamens proximal; stylar column pubescent.
Juice:	SG 1056; acidity 0.23%; tannin 0.24%.
Cider:	No cider-maker's notes found. Improved Hangdown juice is mildly bittersweet and flavourable so should make a fair cider.

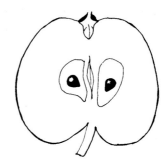

IMPROVED KINGSTON BLACK
Late Sharp
Synonym: Port Wine.

Although the name would presume this variety to be even better than the legendary Kingston Black, this is unfortunately completely untrue. It is relatively disease free, certainly a major improvement, but Improved Kingston Black is a sharp, lacking in tannin, which makes an indifferent cider only. It is definitely not to be confused with the balanced bittersharp qualities of the true Kingston Black. It is more likely to be related to Black Vallis, a very similar apple. First records at Long Ashton are from fruit sent in by Squire Neville Grenville of Butleigh Court in 1908, after which it was planted in several trial orchards. It has been described as 'a good sort', and was regarded as one of the best 'all rounders' by those who grew it at the time. It still crops up in orchards around Butleigh, and at Glastonbury, Baltonsborough, West Bradley and elsewhere.

Mature trees can be quite large and spreading. They carry a full head of leaves, dark and free of disease. It certainly crops better and is less disease susceptible than Kingston Black proper. It flowers in early May.

The fruits which mature in late October, are a similar size and shape to Kingston Black, rather flattened. They are also almost completely covered in a dark red flush which is never so dense, or so black, but more cherry red.

Size:	Medium to large, 55 to more than 60mm.
Shape:	Cylindrical or flattened conical almost oblate, broad nose and base; tending to ribbed.
Stem:	Absent or a thick fleshy stub; basin small, narrow, absent in king fruit.
Eye:	Basin small, narrow, usually smooth but tending to crowned, occasionally beaded; sepals short, broad.
Skin:	Pale yellow, dry or slightly waxy.
Flush:	Always present, virtually complete, strong bright red or pink, to dark red, faintly striped; skin colour showing only in stem basin.
Flesh:	Sharp, hard, melting dessert texture, white, vascular strands red, reddened under skin.
Core:	Small, median, usually open, often 6 loculi; tube a deep, narrow cone or funnel.
Juice:	Sharp, variable acidity. SG 1056; acidity 0.30-80%; tannin 0.15%.
Cider:	A mild sharp cider with a rather insipid flavour.

IMPROVED LAMBROOK PIPPIN
Early Mild Sharp

Hailing from the village of Lambrook in central Somerset, near Martock, Lambrook Pippin is one of a family of similar cider apples selected for local cider making; Porter's Perfection, Cap of Liberty and probably also Kingston Black. It's cider making qualities are good but its fruits are rather small. This *protégé* of Lambrook Pippin certainly improved on fruit size, but not necessarily on taste. The Improved version is a mild sharp, lacking in astringency and with a rather dessert character. It was introduced for Taunton Cider in the '60s and appears as bush trees in many plantings in Somerset the last half of the century but is by no means common.

This noticeably early flowering variety is often in full bloom at the end of April. It is sometimes easily spotted in a bush orchard by the brush of suckers which sprout around the base of each tree. It is vigorous and spreading, the stronger branches carrying some bare wood.

The fruit is large and attractive, with yellow skin and bright red stripes, a long stalk and prominent lenticels. It is a useful, early maturing variety which is ready by the end of September or early October. Unfortunately it is thin skinned and rather prone to codling moth attack so easily rots if left too long on the ground.

Size:	Large, 55 to more than 60mm.
Shape:	Round or flattened cylindrical; slightly angular.
Stem:	Long, green-yellow, woody, projecting distinctly from a large, deep and steep basin.
Eye:	Basin absent or very slight, slightly bumpy or beaded; calyx open, sepals upright in a free crown.
Skin:	Pale primrose yellow; smooth, rather greasy; russet occasionally in basins; lenticels very conspicuous as dots or with a pale surround on the flush.
Flush:	Always, from 20-75%, carmine flecks and stripes over diffuse orange flush.
Flesh:	Dessert character, low acid and sweet; yellowish, sometimes red under the skin, melting or crisp texture.
Core:	Small; tube a medium to large cone.
Juice:	SG 1067; acidity 0.50%; tannin 0.08%.
Cider:	No cider-maker's comments found.

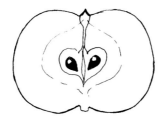

IMPROVED WOODBINE
Late Sweet

This apple is probably a seedling of the true Woodbine for it is similar in many ways. It is hardly an improvement though, since it is very vigorous and unmanageable in its tree habit whilst also being very susceptible to scab and canker.

The trees are large and unwieldy, with many extremely upright branches carrying much bare wood. It is so susceptible to scab that it is frequently defoliated by mid summer.

The fruits, which mature in early November, look very similar to the true Woodbine. They are flattened conical with a short stubby stem, and covered with a dark, slightly striped maroon coloured flush.

Size: Fairly large, 50-60mm.
Shape: Flattened conical, tending to oblate, nose broad, base flattened; rounded, often irregular with scab.
Stem: Thick fleshy stub, within or just projecting from a small, shallow basin.
Eye: Basin broad but shallow, smooth, sometimes beaded; calyx open, sepals short, upright.
Skin: Green; smooth, dry; very scab susceptible; lenticels prominent dots.
Flush: Always, 50-80%, diffuse, slightly striped dark carmine red.
Flesh: Mildly acidic sweet, rather non-descript; chewy or melting; greenish with green vascular strands.
Core: Medium, median, axile; tube a cone, sometimes large.
Cider: No cider-maker's notes found, but unlikely to contribute much to any cider.

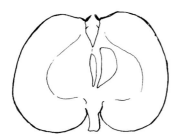

KING'S FAVOURITE
Mid season sharp

Although the original and only fruit sample sent to Long Ashton for a cider making trial, was from Melplash, Dorset in 1927, this variety still crops up from time to time in old orchards around the Glastonbury and Shepton Mallet area. It has a genuine sharp cider flavour which is not typical of Somerset. There is a record of several un-named apples coming to the Research Station from a Mr King of Berkley, Gloucestershire in 1908. The juice of King's Favourite does compare with his sample called No.2, and tastes similar to a mild, Foxwhelp type of typical Gloucester apple. It is pure conjecture, but King's Favourite could possibly have originated as a seedling from an apple of that type.

King's Favourite is a medium to large sized, rather angular, flattened conical fruit, pale green with conspicuous bright red stripes. The stem is fairly stout and short.

Size: Medium, 45-60mm.
Shape: Flat conical; angular, often ribbed.
Stem: Usually within the cavity, occasionally projecting slightly from a small, broad basin.
Eye: Basin smallish, fairly smooth, occasionally slightly crowned; calyx sometimes slightly open, sepals short, green.
Skin: Light green ripening to almost white; smooth and waxy; russet slight in stem cavity, occasionally streaky.
Flush: Usual but dependant on sunlight reaching fruits; from a trace to 75%, slight to strong, short stripes of bright red and crimson carmine.
Flesh: Sharp; juicy, white.
Core: Medium, median; tube a broad cone, sometimes open towards core as a slit.
Juice: SG 1053; acidity 0.96%; tannin 0.12%.
Cider: No cider-maker's notes found, but King's Favourite juice is well flavoured and sharp, so should make a good addition to any cider.

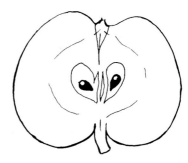

KINGSTON BLACK
Late Mid-season Bittersharp
Synonym: Black Taunton, now dropped in favour of Kingston Black.

Kingston Black, thought to be named after the village of Kingston St Mary, near Taunton, is probably related to other Somerset bittersharp varieties such as Cap of Liberty, Lambrook Pippin and Porter's Perfection. It reached almost legendary status in the late twentieth century as a vintage cider apple, although to many, this fame is somewhat exaggerated. Kingston Black juice is bittersharp with well balanced tannin and acidity. Fruit from old standard trees is often high in sugar and will make a full bodied, single variety cider with a distinctive flavour. Because of its popularity it was widely planted throughout all the cider growing regions, but its performance varies considerably depending on soil types and location. Scott's Catalogue in 1873, listed it as 'A handsome grower and a great bearer . . . It is to be found in almost every orchard in this neighbourhood' [mid Somerset]. Recent bush orchard plantings have been rather disappointing and have not achieved quite the same vintage quality. However, it is still planted in limited quantities for the specialist market of Kingston Black cider.

The variety has many faults as an orchard tree; it is over-vigorous, a shy cropper, has poor, malformed, almost stemless flowers overlooked by pollinating insects, and tends to be very susceptible to scab and canker. The mature tree has a thin, open, spreading head formed of long, unbranched limbs. The final size of the tree depends on the incidence of scab and canker to which Kingston Black is very prone.

The shape of the fruit can be quite variable. It is flushed very dark red, sometimes almost black, and has a rich fruity flavour. It matures quite late, in early November.

Size: Medium to small, 45-55mm.
Shape: Variable; basic shape conical or flattened, tending to cylindrical.
Stem: Variable, medium thick, thick fleshy stems common; within the cavity or level with the base; basin rather narrow and shallow but sometimes deep.
Eye: Well defined shallow or deep and steep sided, sometimes slightly puckered; calyx slightly open, sepals free.
Skin: Yellow-green; dry, rather rough; russet spreading slightly to the cheek, sometimes forming a network, usually scaly in the stem basin; lenticels conspicuous, large, irregular, often surrounded by a light area.
Flush: Always more than 75%, often complete, flecked or slightly striped very dark red, almost black.
Flesh: Bittersharp, mildly acidic with some astringency which is often not marked, rich fruity almost dessert flavour; reddened, sometimes white; dry, floury.

Core: Slightly proximal or median; axile, loculi often open, rather small; tube conical; stamens median.
Juice: SG 1061; acidity 0.58%; tannin 0.19%.
Cider: Kingston Black's juice is bittersharp with well balanced tannin and acidity which will make a full bodied, single variety cider with a distinctive flavour. The results from fruit from young trees may be disappointing, since, like all varieties, its vintage qualities improve with maturity. The juice is slow to ferment.

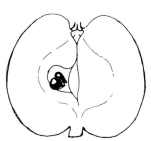

LAMBROOK PIPPIN
Late Mid-season Bittersharp

This variety was first recorded at the Bath and West Show in 1895, from a sample of fruit sent in from Martock described as a very useful late cider apple. Lambrook Pippin is related to Porter's Perfection, Kingston Black and Cap of Liberty and naturally makes cider of excellent quality; bittersharp with superior flavour and aroma. It originated in Somerset [reputedly from Symes of Martock], and may have started out as an eating apple. It was often used as a stem builder and mainframe in orchards in that part of the county. Its strong vigorous growth often outgrew the top-worked variety and trees, part Lambrook Pippin, part another weaker variety, are quite common in old orchards.

On its own it forms a fair sized tree, strong and with dense, vigorous growth. It is renowned for its remarkable powers of regeneration. It is slow to come into cropping and biennial but makes a large tree and crops well when bearing. It flowers mid to late May.

The fruit, which matures in November, is medium sized, flattened and rounded, flushed pinkish-orange with red flecks and conspicuous lenticels. The eye is often a distinctive feature, wide open with prominent reflexed sepals. Lambrook Pippin fruit will sometimes twin like its offspring Porter's Perfection.

Size: Small to medium, 40-55mm.
Shape: Oblate flattened rounded, base rounded; sometimes irregular with scab; twinning occasionally.
Stem: Level with base or projecting distinctly, usually fairly thick, fleshy, sometimes with a strig; stem basin fairly small and shallow.
Eye: Basin small, shallow, sometimes slightly puckered and ribbed; calyx open, sepals fairly long, often free, and reflexed at tips.
Skin: Yellowish green; smooth, slightly waxy; very scab susceptible; lenticels usually small but conspicuous, surrounded by a light area, sometimes corky.
Flush: About 60%, pinkish-orange heavily flecked with red, sometimes slightly striped.
Flesh: Sharp with some tannin; greenish white, woolly, juicy and hard.
Core: Tube a small cone; seeds large.
Juice: SG 1055, acidity 0.58%, tannin 0.24%.
Cider: Lambrook Pippin makes a nice light cider of excellent quality, flavour and superior aroma. Fermentation is usually slow.

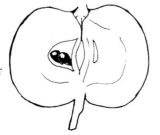

LANGWORTHY
Late Sharp
Synonyms: Wyatt's Seedling or Sweet, Sour Natural [in Devon].

Langworthy is usually recorded as a Devon apple for this is its usual name in that county, but Langworthy and Wyatt's Seedling are undoubtedly one and the same. Mr Wyatt from Kingweston in south Somerset often sent this variety in for cider making competitions at the Cider Institute in the 1930s, sometimes naming it Wyatt's Sweet in spite of its sharp taste. It was also called Wyatt's Seedling in Newton St Cyres in Devon where it grew in several orchards, but towards the end of the 1930s, fruit from this locality was consistently called Langworthy. In the 1932 Cider Competition at Long Ashton, Langworthy won first prize as a mild sharp. Afterwards enjoying some popularity, it was widely planted from Exeter to Crediton, Taunton to Sutton Montis, and at Whiteways own orchard in Whimple, Devon. It is not so popular nowadays in bush orchards, mostly because of it small sized fruits.

This variety is reputed to be a good cropper but rather mildew susceptible. Growth may be slow in early years but mature trees are large and spreading. It flowers in early May.

The small, neat rounded fruits with tiny stem and eye basins, are not ready until early November. They are flushed bright red and covered with a distinctive patterned russet and dots.

Size: Very variable, usually medium but often small, less than 40-55mm.
Shape: Rounded or flattened conical, sometimes with a nose, base broad; regular.
Stem: Usually fairly stout but can be long and thin; stem basin small, often almost absent.
Eye: Basin slight, puckered, lightly ribbed, sometimes a trace of beading; calyx open, sepals free, short, upright, often broken.
Skin: Light greenish-yellow; smooth, slightly waxy; no scab; russet a distinguishing feature, golden, often heavily dotted all over, associated with lenticels.
Flush: More than 60%; bright red, flecked and slightly striped dark maroon.
Flesh: Mild sharp sometimes with some astringency; crisp, white.
Core: Small, median, axile; tube a deep cone or funnel often extending to core.
Juice: SG 1051; acidity 0.47%; tannin 0.12%.
Cider: Langworthy makes a pleasant, brisk, light, sweet cider with a good flavour and aroma, but rather body deficient. Useful alone or blended.

LE BRET
Mid Season Sweet

Le Bret was named after Mrs Le Bret of Bristol who brought some apples to Long Ashton in 1956. It proved to be an interesting sweet cider apple, similar to the Devon variety, Killerton Sweet, and was included in the orchard trials in the 1950s. Le Bret was widely planted in both the South West and in Hereford in the 1970s, perhaps more by mistake than by intent. It was planted under the name Sweet Alford, a variety which it only superficially resembles. This was most probably a simple mistake made during the propagation of trees for new bush orchards at the time, but it is still referred to as Sweet Alford in many orchards.

Le Bret is moderately vigorous and makes a medium to large tree with a dense spreading head. It flowers very early in late April. It is easy to train as a bush tree with a strong, dominant centre leader, but spurring is only moderate.

Le Bret is ready by mid to late October. Its fruits are large and bold, yellow flushed with bright scarlet, and have distinctly upright sepals. Sweet Alford fruits are usually smaller, less bright and have a much longer stalk.

Size: Large, 55 to more than 60mm.
Shape: Conical-cylindrical, nose and base broad.
Stem: Within or usually projecting slightly or distinctly from a deep, steep basin.
Eye: Basin variable, small or narrow and deep, slightly furrowed or crowned; calyx more or less open, sepals upright, reflexed at tips, often green.
Skin: Primrose yellow or pale green; dry, rough; russet often scabrous in eye basin, spreading; lenticels large, russeted.
Flush: Always, 30-65%, bright scarlet with crimson flecks.
Flesh: Sweet without astringency; yellowish, vascular strands yellow; chewy.
Core: Median, axile; tube often deep and open to the core.
Juice: SG 1054; acidity 0.20%; tannin 0.12%.
Cider: No cider-maker's notes, but Le Bret is likely to make a soft, pleasant and light cider on its own.

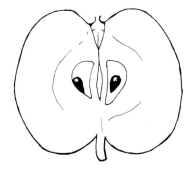

LONG TOM
Early Mid Season Mild Sharp

This variety is probably a speciality peculiar to the North West corner of Somerset, Clevedon to Weston, Kingston Seymour and Congresbury area. It resembles an elongated version of the familiar Tom Putt and could well be a seedling from it, saved and cultivated for its curious distinctive shape.

The unmistakable fruits are large, red and elliptical, with ten strongly marked ribs from top to bottom. The flesh is marbled with red throughout and the core is large and hollow so that the pips rattle when the fruits are ripe.

Long Tom is an early maturing dual purpose, mild sharp apple, ready by early October. It would only be useful for cider making when blended with juice from other fruit.

Size: Large, 55-60mm in diameter and up to 70mm tall.
Shape: Elliptical, small nose, small rounded base; strongly 10 ribbed from eye to stem basin.
Stem: Projecting distinctly, rather fleshy, bulge at the tree end; basin medium, rather narrow and deep.
Eye: Basin slight, crowned, beaded and irregular similar to Tom Putt; calyx open, sepals short and closed.
Skin: Pale yellow; rough and waxy; russet slight in each basin; lenticels small brown dots on lighter surround.
Flush: Usually more or less complete; diffuse pink with bright red flecks, short stripes.
Flesh: Mild sharp; juicy and melting, white, distinctly reddened under skin.
Core: Open, abaxile, large; seeds numerous, free rattling when ripe; tube a very deep cone extending to the core; stamens distal; pronounced stylar column.
Juice: Mild sharp.
Cider: No cider-maker's notes found, but Long Tom would be a useful mild sharp for blending.

LORNA DOONE
Early Bittersharp

This cider apple came to Long Ashton in the 1930s from Mr E.H. Wells of Wellington, the home of Lorna Doone Cider. The Long Ashton Report for 1935 gave it a Prize as a good, medium sharp cider, and mentions its reputation as a heavy cropper. It was considered especially interesting because of this and its high tannin content, but in spite of further successful cider trials, Lorna Doone did not catch on. It does not seem to have been propagated much outside its native locality. Some trees exist in a Trial orchard in Hereford, and it is represented in the dessert apple section of the Brogdale Collection.

Lorna Doone is a vigorous variety that flowers in early May. The fruits which are ready in early October, are fairly large, flattened-conical with a stout stem in a broad deep basin. The skin is pale yellowish, flushed brown and lightly striped bright red, similar to Somerset Redstreak.

Size:	Medium to large, 55 to more than 60mm.
Shape:	Flattened conical, broad base and nose; tending to ribbed.
Stem:	Short, stout, within a broad, deep basin.
Eye:	Basin medium, fairly deep, narrow; rather crowned and ribbed, ribs sometimes extending down the sides; calyx open, sepals upright.
Skin:	Pale yellowish-green; greasy; russet dots and patches.
Flush:	About 60%, pale brownish-red, streaked bright red.
Flesh:	Mild bittersharp, sweet and lightly flavoured; soft, mealy; white.
Juice:	SG 1060; acidity 0.43%; tannin 0.31%.
Cider:	Lorna Doone makes rather a strong flavoured cider with a harsh tannin character. It is best blended and should be a useful 'extender' for low tannin mixtures.

MAJOR
Early Bittersweet

Major is a typical Somerset 'jersey' apple which probably arose in the central part of the county, but is also found in many traditional Devon cider orchards. It is an old variety which was included from time to time in trial orchards often dating pre-1920. It was not extensively planted for a while after this because of its early harvesting season, difficult to fit in with traditional farming practices.

Recently, in the late 1980s and 90s, there has been a trend towards extending the harvesting season forward to the end of September and very early October. Major's early maturity has now become a useful asset for planting together with the other earlies, Ashton Bitter, Ellis Bitter and sometimes White Jersey in bush orchards.

Major is a vigorous variety and quickly forms a big tree. As a standard it forms a medium to large sized, round headed tree with spreading limbs. Bush trees are vigorous, even on the more dwarfing rootstocks, but Major spurs quickly and has a good natural centre leader shape and many spreading branches. Its excessive vigour is difficult to control on strong soils, but it responds by forming spurs on branches that are bent down to encourage early crops.

Flowering time is late mid season. It is rather susceptible to canker and may get some scab.

The fruit is smallish, typical 'jersey' shaped, conical with a pointed nose, and covered in a light pinkish red striped flush. It is ready early and begins to drop before the end of September. The woolly, white flesh has a pleasant fruity flavour with plenty of tannin but the apples do not keep well on the ground.

Size:	Small to medium, rarely large, 45-60mm.
Shape:	Conical, base narrow, nose pointed; sometimes ribbed.
Stem:	Woody, level with the base or projecting distinctly, sometimes slightly, from a small, sometimes slight basin.
Eye:	Basin small, variable, usually shallow, puckered, irregular, usually ribbed, often slight corona present; calyx closed, sepals overlapping, often fairly long, reflexed at tips.
Skin:	Yellowish-green or pale yellow; smooth and slightly waxy; russet usually slight.
Flush:	Usually 35-65% or more, flecked and striped over diffuse, bright red; overall pinkish appearance.
Flesh:	Sweet, astringent with a pleasant flavour; white, woolly, rather soft, juicy.
Core:	Median, loculi open, lateral cracks frequently present;

seeds broad, lemon shaped and numerous; tube deep cone or funnel; stamens usually proximal.

Juice: SG 1054; acidity 0.18%; tannin 0.41%.

Cider: Major is a full bittersweet and make a fruity cider of average quality. It is best blended with other varieties for a more balanced product.

MICHELIN
Mid Season Bittersweet

This is a French variety introduced into Hereford by a Monsieur Legrand for the Woolhope Society in 1884. It was named after a Monsieur Michelin who did much to promote the study of cider fruits. Michelin was extensively planted in Hereford from the 1920s, and is now the most widely planted variety in all the cider growing areas. Although its juice qualities are only modest, it is one of the most reliably annual cropping varieties along with Dabinett, and this is the main reason for its popularity.

Mature standard trees are medium sized with stiff, upright limbs. As a bush tree, it tends to want to be multi-leadered, and needs considerable thought and training in its formative years to produce a good centre-leader shape. Spurring is quick and good, and cropping starts early. Flowering time is 2nd week of May. Unfortunately, it is very prone to canker, especially on some sites and young trees can be almost destroyed by the disease.

Plain green Michelin apples are never very large, rather elongated conical with a small nose and rounded base, and distinctly ribbed. They are mature in mid October but easy enough to shake off earlier if needed.

Size: Medium often small, 40-50mm.

Shape: Conical, cylindrical, sometimes pointed; distinctly ribbed.

Stem: Thick, woody, often fleshy, sometimes off-set, usually projecting considerably, sometimes level with base; stem basin well defined.

Eye: Basin shallow or slight, puckered, often beaded; calyx closed, sepals often green.

Skin: Greenish-yellow to yellow; smooth, slightly waxy; sometimes russet spreads from stem basin to cheek; lenticels often conspicuous; scab susceptible.

Flush: Sometimes, usually slight pinky-orange diffuse.

Flesh: Sweet with some astringency; white, woolly.

Core: Slightly distal, axile, open; tube narrow conical.

Juice: SG 1050; acidity 0.25%; tannin 0.23%.

Cider: Medium bittersweet with soft tannin.

MORGAN SWEET
Early Sweet

Well known to many living in North Somerset, its natural home, Morgan sweet is cherished and extolled from happy childhood memories. It was once widely planted all over Somerset and to a lesser extent in Devon and Gloucestershire, originally intended as a 'pot' fruit, much of it going to South Wales. But once it lost that fresh fruit market, Morgan Sweet had to go for cider making only, then often fetching a lower price than other genuine cider fruits. The fruit matures very early and its juice ferments very rapidly. For some farms and cider-makers Morgan Sweet was popular as a source of early cider, ready for Christmas, well before the main cider had finished maturing properly. Formerly, it had a bad reputation for being unstable as a naturally sweet cider and very susceptible to bacterial disorder, but these troubles were largely overcome with the introduction of better cider making practices.

Since the early part of the century Morgan Sweet has been widely used as a stem builder for standard trees of other varieties. Usually Morgan Sweet stock was not headworked until it was well established with a framework of about ten branches on each of which a single stick was grafted. This strong framework often takes over again in old trees and sometimes the head will be a mixture of Morgan Sweet and a more choice but weaker variety.

Morgan Sweet flowers early to mid season but it is a triploid and for that reason it is useless as a pollinator. It makes very strong growth, forming a big spreading tree with large, scab susceptible leaves.

The fruits are easy to identify as they ripen very early in late August or early September, often dropping and rotting on the ground and going to waste. They are large, pale yellow, rather soft and juicy with a pure sweet taste. Morgan Sweet is described in *The Apple and Pear as Vintage Fruits* as a favourite Somerset apple but note that it is erroneously listed there as late maturing.

Size: Medium to very large, 50 to more than 60mm.
Shape: Conical, base flattened, nose pointed; usually ribbed; king fruits elongated.
Stem: Thin, woody; usually projecting slightly from a medium, shallow basin; king fruit stems thick, fleshy and short.
Eye: Basin medium, shallow, sometimes large and deep, ribbed or puckered; calyx usually closed, sepals touching, free, often green at the base.
Skin: Greenish-yellow; smooth, dry, sometimes slightly waxy; scab susceptible; russet usually confined to stem basin; lenticels often conspicuous, concentrated around the eye.
Flush: Absent, occasionally very slight red flecks spreading from the eye.
Flesh: Sweet with no astringency; white, rather soft and juicy.
Core: Median, axile, loculi open; seeds few; tube usually medium funnel, sometimes conical.
Juice: SG 1049; acidity 0.22%; tannin 0.13%; nitrogen 18mg/100mg [average 5-10mg/100mg].
Cider: Morgan Sweet is a pure sweet. Because of its high nitrogen content the juice will ferment very rapidly. With care it can produce a good quality cider with a strong, persistently fruity flavour but lacking in body.

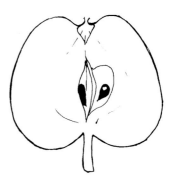

NEVERBLIGHT
Early Medium Sharp
Synonyms: Wildling Neverblight and possibly White Wine and Sour Cadbury.

Fruit came from the villages of Woolston and Cadbury, in the Yeovil area, to Long Ashton early in the century. It was considered good enough to plant some trees there in 1914 so that the cider could be made regularly. These trees were still at Long Ashton as late as 1952. It was also planted extensively in the old Long Ashton trial orchards around Somerset and Hereford. Neverblight still stands as big old trees in some of these orchards today.

Trees are a fair size with a round head, moderately vigorous, upright and spreading. Cropping is above average, heavy but biennial. As its name implies, it is quite resistant to scab. Flowering time is mid May.

The fruit looks similar to Cadbury from which it is distinguished by its sharp taste with a hint of astringency. Neverblight matures early and is usually ready by late September to early October. The fruits are a Reinette type, medium sized, rather russeted conical apples, usually with some pinkish flush.

Size: Medium to large, 55 to more than 60mm.
Shape: Conical with broad nose, flat base; tending to ribbed.
Stem: Very short, within or projecting slightly from narrow, deep basin.
Eye: Basin small, smooth and regular, occasionally tending to crowned; sepals often slightly open, often green.
Skin: Pale yellow; heavy russet network spreading from the nose; lenticels small dots sometimes associated with russet patches.
Flush: Usually present, less than 50%; diffuse pinkish-red or orange.
Flesh: Mild sharp; chewy, yellowish, browning rapidly.
Core: Small, slightly proximal, open; tube a small cone.
Juice: SG 1052, acidity 0.55%; tannin 0.15-22%.
Cider: Neverblight cider was first described in 1906 as sweet, slightly sharp, having a moderate flavour without much character and useful for blending. It was later described as medium brisk with an attractive character in favourable seasons.

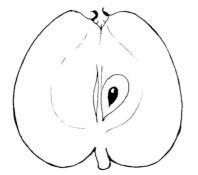

NORTON BITTERS
Late Full Bittersweet
Synonym: Nerton Bitter.

Norton Bitters was recorded for the Bath and West Show in 1895 as growing in Mr F.J. Hayes' Orchard in West Pennard, and a contemporary watercolour of it together with three other old Somerset cider apples, still hangs on the wall of the Secretary's Office at the Showground at Shepton Mallet. Trees still exist in this area and it was also planted in one or two places in Hereford by H.P. Bulmer after fruit was brought to Long Ashton in 1964 for successful trials. It was never propagated extensively in either county although it probably deserves to be more widely planted.

Norton Bitters apples are dark red-maroon, rather cylindrical in shape, with very small eye and stem basins. They are often covered with patches of russet. The taste is a good, often full bittersweet, but maturing in November makes the variety rather too late for general orchard use.

Size: Medium, usually 45-55mm.
Shape: Flattened conical or cylindrical; rounded or slightly angular, sometimes slightly lopsided.
Stem: Usually a stub within the cavity, sometimes projecting slightly from a small, narrow basin; stem basin non-existent or very slight in king fruit.
Eye: Basin small or slight, narrow and shallow, smooth or irregularly beaded; sepals short, green.
Skin: Yellow; smooth or rough, dry or slightly waxy; russet often spreading from eye, patches or network over cheek.
Flush: Always more than two thirds, often more or less complete; dark red diffuse, striped bright red, some fruits only lightly striped with no diffuse.
Flesh: Bittersweet, mild or full bitter with good flavour; melting when ripe, white or greenish, sometimes reddened near nose.
Core: Medium, often slightly distal, axile, open; tube a cone, sometimes quite deep and narrow, reaching core.
Juice: SG 1068; acidity 0.26%; tannin 23%.
Cider: No comments are recorded at Long Ashton, but Norton Bitter is a medium to full bittersweet with good flavour and aroma, so should make a pleasant single variety cider or blend usefully with other varieties.

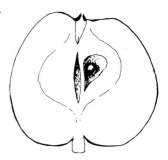

PENNARD BITTER
Early Bittersweet
Synonym: Possibly Meare Bitter but this may be a similar variety.

Named after the village of West Pennard near Shepton Mallet in Somerset, Pennard Bitter is said to have been propagated by Harold Heal of Windmill Hill, Glastonbury, probably towards the end of the nineteenth century.

It makes a vigorous, spreading bush tree and seems to crops well and regularly but is hardly ever grown on a dwarfing stock. It could be useful in bush orchards and probably deserves to be grown more widely as an early harvesting variety.

Pennard Bitter ripens early in October. It is typically a large green fruit, flattened and angular with brownish red russeted flush and a very short stalk.

Size: Large to very large, 55 to more than 60mm.
Shape: Oblate conical, nose rounded, base broad; rather angular, distinctly ribbed.
Stem: Thick, green and fleshy stub within the cavity; basin small, tight.
Eye: Basin medium, narrow, deep, furrowed; calyx closed, sepals long.
Skin: Yellowish-green; usually smooth and dry, sometimes rough with russet; russet slight, sometimes considerable, spreading from both cavities as a light network over the flush.
Flush: Always 30-65%, diffuse dark orange red or brown, resembling Cox.
Flesh: Medium bittersweet; juicy, chewy, greenish, browning rapidly when cut.
Core: Median, medium, open, large axial sack; seeds many; tube a large cone; stamens distal.
Juice: SG 1060; acidity 0.18%; tannin 0.32%.
Cider: No cider-maker's notes have been found but Pennard Bitter looks like a useful bittersweet with plenty of tannin, suitable for blending with other varieties.

PIG'S SNOUT
Mid Season Dual Purpose
Synonyms: Sheep's Nose, Larland. Sometimes incorrectly called Ponsford in Somerset.

This old apple variety is very likely the Sheep's Nose mentioned by Hogg as 'a very handsome-looking apple, and of remarkable shape.' Hogg called it a cider apple, also good for cooking, having described the flesh as tender, juicy and sweet with a mild acidity.

Pig's Snout usually occurs as single trees in old orchards, especially in east and mid Somerset, around Shepton and Glastonbury. Trees are well shaped but weak and prone to scab and canker.

This is a most colourful apple, large, shiny and strongly red striped. It is easy to see how its gets its name, with its distinctive ribs and five crowned snouts almost as broad as their bases. Sometimes the seeds will rattle if the fruits are shaken when they are quite ripe towards the end of October.

Size: Large, usually more than 60mm.
Shape: Elongated conical, waisted with a broad nose and base; distinctly ribbed.
Stem: Projecting slightly, often just a stub, woody; basin medium, broad and deep.
Eye: Basin medium, crowned and often beaded; ribs extending over cheeks; calyx usually open, sepals short, upright.
Skin: Pale green or yellow; smooth, greasy; russet usually confined to stem cavity; scab susceptible.
Flush: Always more than 50%; covered with bright red flecks and stripes over scarlet diffuse.
Flesh: Mild sharp, sweet but with a rather culinary flavour; texture melting; yellowish often reddened under the skin.
Core: Median, axile, large; seeds often few, rattling when ripe; tube a broad cone open to core.
Juice: Mildly acidic with high sugar content.
Cider: No cider-maker's comments found. The cider is likely to be thin and sharp but useful for blending with varieties of more body.

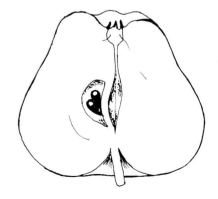

POOR MAN'S PROFIT
Dual Purpose
Synonyms; Profit Apple, Profit.

Profit is a culinary or dual purpose apple which was once probably fairly widespread in the West Country. It was mentioned in *The Apples of England* and numerous other places as a Somerset apple, with earliest records dating from 1824. It can be seen growing in the dessert and culinary section of the Brogdale Fruit Collection.

Profit trees are moderately vigorous and flower in May. Their fruit is large and handsome, distinctly waisted or with a nose. The skin is green with distinct bright red stripes. The flesh is said to be rich and sweet enough to keep its shape when cooked. Ready in late October or November, Profit apples may be rather prone to bitter pit.

Size: Very large, 60 to more than 70mm.
Shape: Conical, waisted, base broad.
Stem: Short, level with the base or within the cavity; basin medium but deep.
Eye: Basin small, smooth or slightly bumpy; calyx usually wide open; sepals free.
Skin: Greenish-yellow; smooth and waxy; russet sometimes spreading as light network from stem cavity; lenticels conspicuous on some fruits as small brown dots.
Flush: Always 50-75%; strongly striped bright red over a light diffuse flush.
Flesh: Dessert flavour, sub-acid; juicy and melting, greenish with green vascular strands.
Core: Slightly proximal, open; seeds numerous; tube a large cone.
Cider: No cider-maker's notes found. As Poor Man's Profit is a dual purpose apple, its cider is likely to be rather thin and non-descript but blend well with bittersweet cider apples.

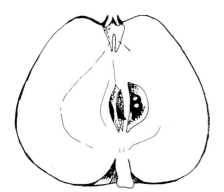

PORTER'S PERFECTION
Late Medium Bittersharp
Synonym: Clusters.

This variety originated in nurseryman Mr Charles Porter's orchard at East Lambrook during the nineteenth century. Some fruit from the original tree was sent to Long Ashton in 1907 where it was judged remarkable for the quality of its juice. From this start it was quickly propagated and distributed around some of the early trial orchards, and again in the 1957 series of trials. Porter's Perfection is common in the Martock area of Somerset and appears less regularly in other parts of the county.

This variety is closely related to Lambrook Pippin and its fruits are very similar. Porter's Perfection is a vigorous grower with a spreading habit and drooping branches. Mature trees are large to medium sized and produce heavy crops of small fruit. Flowering time is early May.

Porter's Perfection is late and not ready for harvest until the third week of November. Its fruits are small and dark red with conspicuously light spots round the lenticels. It is remarkable for regularly producing fused fruits, usually two together, sometimes three to five in one. This curious phenomena also occurs more rarely in the varieties Lambrook Pippin, Dabinett and Somerset Redstreak.

Size: Small, sometimes medium, 40-50mm.
Shape: Flattened conical or conical; some fused fruits consisting of 2-5 apples usually present.
Stem: Thick, slightly fleshy, often green, projecting considerably, sometimes slightly from a small, shallow, often irregular basin.
Eye: Basin shallow; calyx open, sepals fairly long, upright and reflexed at tips.
Skin: Greenish-yellow; smooth, slightly waxy; russet slight in the stem basin; lenticels conspicuous, small, surrounded by lighter patch on flush, or green patch where flush is absent; reputedly scab resistant.
Flush: More than two thirds, usually absent from the shaded portions of the fruit, flecked and striped dark red.
Flesh: Mild sharp with some astringency; white or greenish-white, sometimes reddened below skin, crisp and juicy.
Core: Median, axile, usually closed; seeds numerous; tube a shallow cone.
Juice: SG 1054; acidity 0.82%; tannin 0.25%.
Cider: Porter's Perfection can produce an excellent cider. Its juice is rather acidic bittersharp and is better blended for a more balanced product.

RED JERSEY
Mid Season Bittersweet
Synonyms: Laurel Grange, also Loral or Loyal Drain or Drang!

A typical small Somerset 'jersey' apple. Trees are still found commonly around the Shepton Mallet to Glastonbury area. The curious synonyms arose through misspellings or mis-hearings of the local dialect. It used to be called Laurel Grange after Mr Wilfred Naish's farm, The Grange, West Pennard, near Shepton Mallet. Many old trees are still cropping well in orchards round about, together with many similar small red sorts. This would suggest that Red Jersey probably originated in this locality, and indeed it was recorded at the Bath and West Show in 1895 from West Pennard. Trees also still occur in some of the old Long Ashton trial orchards and in farm orchards, mostly in Somerset and adjacent parts of Devon.

Red Jersey trees are quite distinctive. They are medium to large sized with a spreading habit and a heavy complex system of twigs and spurs forming a dense crown. Its leaves are also distinctive, numerous, narrow and rather greyish in appearance. It is a late flowering variety and cropping is heavy but biennial. Red Jersey makes a fair bittersweet cider with strong astringent tannin. Unfortunately its good vintage qualities are let down by its susceptibility to scab and the small size of the fruit. It has a tendency to drop prematurely in an on year, before the apples are properly mature, which should not be before mid October . The fruit is small, conical and flushed bright red.

Fruit: Small, 40-55mm.
Shape: Conical, narrow with a rather pointed nose; rounded.
Stem: Small, woody, projecting slightly from a small, narrow basin.
Eye: Basin small to medium, puckered, sometimes ribbed, sometimes the ribs extend a short distance over cheek.
Skin: Greenish-yellow; smooth, dry; russet confined to stem basin, sometimes scaly; lenticels conspicuous; variable in size, small pale area surrounding; scab susceptible.
Flush: Always more than 75%; flecked, slightly diffuse red, sometimes dull, brownish red.
Flesh: Sweet and astringent; white, slightly crisp, juicy.
Core: Axile, loculi usually open; seeds numerous, brown pointed and filling core; tube conical, rather deep; stylar column often fleshy and green.
Juice: SG 1052; acidity 0.20%; tannin 0.48%.
Cider: Medium to full bittersweet. Good quality cider, full bodied but with strong bitter tannin too pronounced to use alone. Sugar content is average and fermentation slow.

RED WORTHY
Late Mid Season Sweet

This variety probably originated in the Stembridge to Martock area of central Somerset where it has been recorded since 1914. Earliest records at Long Ashton are of fruit sent from Mr Porter of South Petherton, from whose nursery Red Worthy may have originated. A few big old trees still stand in some mixed orchards in Stembridge.

Red Worthy forms a large upright spreading tree. Its head is formed of numerous, layered drooping branches clothed in large leaves. Flowering time is mid May.

The apples which are rather knobbly and angular, have an overall, bright red flush and sometimes give off an interesting banana aroma when ripe in late October. Unfortunately no cider making trials were recorded so it is not known if this flavour comes through into the cider.

Size: Small to medium, 45-55mm.
Shape: Conical, broad nose, rounded base; angular and ribbed.
Stem: Long, thick and woody, projecting considerably, sometimes slightly from a large, deep basin.
Eye: Basin small, sometimes puckered and irregularly crowned, some beading round the eye; calyx slightly open, sepals long and overlapping.
Skin: Light green to greenish yellow, smooth and waxy; lenticels with conspicuous white surrounds away from the flush; scab susceptible.
Flush: Always 60-90% diffuse bright red, very slightly striped dark red.
Flesh: Mild bittersweet; white rather crisp, juicy; with a banana-like aroma.
Core: Median, axile, sometimes open but often closed; seeds numerous; tube conical, often large.
Juice: SG 1053, acidity 0.22%, tannin 0.18%.
Cider: No cider-maker's comments found.

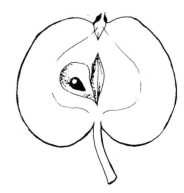

ROYAL JERSEY
Late Full Bittersweet
Synonym: Royal Jersey I.

A bittersweet 'jersey' apple from the mid Somerset area, Royal Jersey was widely planted throughout the county and is still seen in many orchards. This variety belongs to a group of 'jerseys' all with very similar fruit, distinguished by their taste and time of maturity. This variety, named by Prof. Barker at Long Ashton, Royal Jersey [I], is a full bittersweet, not maturing until late October. Early Red Jersey, also known as Royal Jersey [II], answers to the same description, but its taste is only mildly bittersweet, lacking the heavy tannin of this Royal Jersey [I], and its fruit is ready to use by early or mid October. Red Jersey, another small red, medium bittersweet, matures sometime between these two, but its distinctively spreading trees are easily recognised by their narrow grey-green leaves.

Royal Jersey trees are large and rather upright. Growth is slow but cropping is fair. It flowers in late May and fruit is ready in late October or early November. The apples are typical smallish 'jerseys'; striped bright red, conical with a rounded base and distinctly pointed nose.

Size: Medium or small, 45-55mm.
Shape: Conical, base rounded, tending to a nose; rounded, regular.
Stem: Stem projecting slightly, rather woody; basin small, deep, narrow with some russet.
Eye: Basin flattened, medium size, slightly puckered; calyx more or less closed, sepals long and upright.
Skin: Yellow to dull dark green; lenticels often conspicuous on the base of fruit; russet spreading from the stem basin.
Flush: Usual, 30-75% flecked and striped, bright and dark red.
Flesh: Full bittersweet; white, dry, chewy texture.
Core: Median, large, usually abaxile; tube large, conical, deep.
Juice: SG 1062, acidity 0.21%, tannin 0.55%.
Cider: Royal Jersey cider is full bodied bittersweet, pleasantly fruity, slightly bitter but with a rich flavour and good aroma. It is useful for blending. Sugar content is often above average and fermentation slow to moderate.

ROYAL SOMERSET
Late Dual Purpose
Synonym: Incorrectly called London or Louden Pippin.

Hogg describes this variety as 'a very excellent culinary apple'. He quite clearly states that it was a Somerset apple, given to him by a Mr James Lake, nurseryman of Bridgwater in 1847, and it was not to be confused with London [or Louden] Pippin as was misquoted by the RHS at the time. Royal Somerset is a very different apple, sharp, not sweet as described in the National Apple Register. It is a traditional dual purpose apple, useful for either cooking or cider-making. Long Ashton reported that it made a first class medium sharp cider.

Trees of this variety are vigorous, but with a fairly good habit. It flowers mid season and is a partial tip-bearer.

The large and heavy apples are ready by late October. They are fairly distinctly crowned, pale green with a crimson flush, often slightly striped bright red over about two thirds. The eye is very open with short, upright sepals forming a small 'crown'. It was probably this feature which was responsible for the 'royal' epithet. Under this is a distinctively large and deep conical tube.

Size: Large to very large, 60-70mm.
Shape: Cylindrical tending to conical; rather lopsided, slightly ribbed; kings common in some samples.
Stem: Usually thin and woody, thick with a bulge at the base in king fruits, within the cavity or projecting slightly; basin small, narrow and deep, sometimes russeted heavily.
Eye: Basin medium, narrow; bumpy or slightly crowned; calyx open, sepals short, upright.
Skin: Pale green; dry, fairly smooth; russet occasionally heavy in stem basin, then spreading and patchy; lenticels many small brown dots on flush, with pale surround on green.
Flesh: Sharp; greenish, melting and juicy.
Flush: Always 30-65% dark crimson diffuse, with bright red flecks and slight stripes.
Core: Median, axile; seeds numerous; tube a large deep cone.
Juice: SG 1046; acidity 0.71%; tannin 0.11%.
Cider: Recorded as a first class medium sharp.

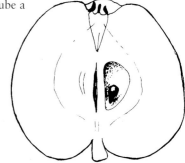

SHARPSHOOTER
Late Mild Bittersharp
Synonyms: Rankshooter, possibly Sparkler.

This variety resembles a typical Gloucestershire Foxwhelp-type of cider apple, rounded, and red striped, tasting sharp with some tannin. It was recently rediscovered by Paul Rendell, a traditional furniture maker of Glastonbury, while collecting cider apples in an old orchard in Baltonsborough for his annual cider-making. Such good quality sharp cider apples are not often found in Somerset, more famous for its bittersweets. Sharpshooter's taste is a pleasant surprise. The clean, sharp attack on the palate is probably how it got its name and reputation. Its origin is speculative. Many 'foreign' cider varieties were introduced into this area through the interest engendered by Squire Neville Grenville of Butleigh Court at the turn of the nineteenth century. Possibly Sharpshooter is a seedling of one of these, a descendant from the Foxwhelp group of vintage cider varieties. It is not ready until late October.

The bright striped apples are medium sized, rounded, with a long, thin stalk and the flesh is red below the skin.

Size:	Medium, 50-60mm, sometimes smaller.
Shape:	Short cylindrical, small rounded nose and base; rounded in section.
Stem:	Woody, projecting distinctly from a small but fairly deep basin.
Eye:	Basin slight, shallow, smooth or partly beaded; calyx open, sepals short.
Skin:	Yellow; smooth and dry; lenticels inconspicuous; russet seldom or slight in stem basin only.
Flush:	Always present, more or less complete, strongly striped bright red.
Flesh:	Sharp with some astringency; chewy cider texture, white but very reddened, vascular strands red.
Core:	Small, median, axile; seeds numerous; tube a small cone extending to a narrow short funnel, occasionally rather deeper and joining core.
Juice:	Sharp or mild bittersharp; SG 1050; acidity 0.31%; tannin 0.25%.
Cider:	No cider-maker's comments found but Sharpshooter should make a useful contribution to a blended cider, perhaps even a creditable single variety cider.

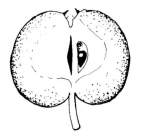

SHEEP'S NOSE
Mid Season Mild Sharp
Synonym: Also called Bell.

This is one of many aptly named cider apples known as Sheep's Nose, a generic name, but this one is distinctive and common enough to be considered a variety. It looks very similar to Bell Apple, which is also known as Sweet Sheep's Nose, but in this case its juice and flesh taste mildly sharp with no astringency. This one is most like the Sheep's Nose in the Brogdale collection, which is Sheep's Nose No.3 of the National Apple Register. It matures quite late in October or November.

The trees are small and whippy, with a weeping habit bearing some bare wood. The large, heavy fruits are conical with a distinct nose, not unlike a large and aromatic Yarlington Mill. Only lightly flushed on the cheek, this Sheep's Nose lacks the attractive strong, pinkish scarlet stripes of the Sheep's Nose, described by Hogg, and the one described here as Pig's Snout.

Size:	Large, 55 to more than 60mm.
Shape:	Variable, basically conical, nose small, base flat, usually convex or distinctly waisted; rather angular.
Stem:	Woody, level with the base or projecting slightly, sometimes reddened; basin deep, narrow.
Eye:	Basin small, narrow, often deep, some fruits with a curious raised line surrounding nose, crowned, somewhat irregular; sepals fairly long, green, more or less upright.
Skin:	Pale yellow-green; rough and dry; russet sometimes spreading in patches or streaks; lenticels small brown dots or large russeted; scab susceptible.
Flush:	Frequently 10-25%, speckled and occasionally slightly striped pinkish-crimson; brownish-orange diffuse flush.
Flesh:	Sub-acid or mild sharp; juicy and melting; vascular strands greenish.
Core:	Large, slightly proximal, open; seeds numerous; tube variable, narrow cone, shallow or extending deeply as a narrow funnel almost to core.
Juice:	SG 1045; acidity 0.25%; tannin 0.17%.
Cider:	No cider-maker's notes found, but Sheep's Nose is unlikely to contribute more than an average dual purpose apple to a cider.

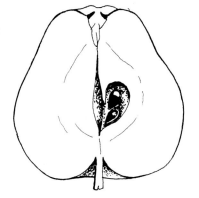

SHOREDITCH WHITE
Early Dual Purpose

Shoreditch White was first described in 1884. It is a useful dual purpose apple both for the kitchen and for making cider. It has little acidity and keeps its shape when cooked. Hogg called it 'a handsome early kitchen apple' and reported that he had received it from a Mr Poynter, nurseryman from Taunton. Shoreditch is a village to the south east of the town. This variety can be seen growing in the National Fruit Collection at Brogdale.

Trees are moderately vigorous. Flowering time is mid May. The apples are flattened conical with a large, deep stem basin. Their colour is distinctive, a delicate cream with a speckled orange blush. Although the fruit matures early, from September to October, it stores reasonably well until November.

Size: Medium, sometimes large, 55 to more than 60mm.
Shape: Very flattened conical, broader than high; rounded, regular.
Stem: Thick, fleshy stub, within the cavity which is distinctly large, broad and deep.
Eye: Basin medium, well defined, smooth, narrow, deep; calyx open, sepals more or less upright, reflexed at tips.
Skin: White or creamy yellow; rough and waxy; russet heavy especially in stem basin, occasionally in eye basin and rough patches across cheeks; lenticels present occasionally as small brown dots.
Flush: Usually trace of orange speckled with bright red on cheek and eye basin.
Flesh: Sweet, rather non-descript; juicy, melting; yellowish.
Core: Small, slightly proximal; tube often a broad rounded cone.
Juice: Mild sharp; typical dual purpose.
Cider: No cider-maker's notes found. Shoreditch White tastes sweet and rather nondescript but would have contributed to average quality farmhouse cider as well as being pleasantly juicy and edible.

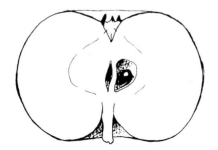

SILVER CUP
Late Mid Season Full Bittersweet

This variety was recorded at the Bath and West Show in 1899 and rated in the early part of the century as a useful bittersweet for blending. It was planted in many orchards in Devon and Somerset where it is still found as old trees, and was included in several trial orchards. It probably originated in south east Somerset, around Wincanton. Early records at Long Ashton were from fruit sent from this region between 1904-11, when it was obviously prized for the strength of its tannin.

It is only grown as standard trees which are very upright and twiggy with many thin shoots and characteristically small leaves. Rather slow to form a tree, Silver Cup is shy at first but produces heavy crops every other year later. Flowering time is early to mid May.

The size of the apples is variable. They can be large in light years or very small with heavy crops. They are pale yellow and cylindrical with a noticeably deep-set eye, and ready for harvest from mid to late October but rot quickly on the ground.

Size: Variable, usually small, 40mm to very large, more than 60mm.
Shape: Cylindrical, base broad; lopsided, angular with distinct ribs.
Stem: Thick and woody, variable, within the basin or sometimes projecting distinctly; basin large and deep, or medium and shallow.
Eye: Basin small, narrow, deep, irregular, furrowed or slightly beaded; calyx closed, sepals long, reflexed, green at the base.
Skin: Pale yellow; smooth, slightly waxy or dry; no longer scab resistant; sometimes light russet, slight in stem cavity; lenticels conspicuous with pale surround or mauvish spots on flush.
Flush: Usually less than 30%; diffuse brown to orange yellow.
Flesh: Bittersweet; chewy; greenish, browning rapidly; fruit do not keep well.
Core: Large, median, axile, sometimes only 3-4 loculi, occasionally more than 5; many large seeds; tube rounded, medium; stamens proximal.
Juice: SG 1075, acidity 0.15%, tannin 0.34%.
Cider: Silver Cup makes a medium dry cider, rich and full bodied with a marked bitterness. It has a pleasant aroma and good flavour but a hard tannin aftertaste. The juice sugar content is often high but fermentation slow. This variety is very useful for blending.

SLACK-MA-GIRDLE
Late Sweet
Synonyms: Slack-my-Girl, Woodbine.

To be worthy of such a name, this variety must have earned a reputation for being at least therapeutic to the digestive systems of the regular imbibers! It is also reputed to make good jam! As a cider apple, it resembles Woodbine both in looks and in the final product, and is sometimes incorrectly called by that name. Slack-ma-Girdle is probably more frequently seen in Devon orchards.

The different tree habits are the best distinguishing feature. Slack-ma-Girdle trees have a relatively compact head with numerous limbs, whereas Woodbine trees are generously open with a few long spreading limbs. Trees of Slack-ma-Girdle are strong, a good size, upright at first then spreading with crops.

The apples of both are broad and flattened with a similar pinkish striped flush, but if seen together, and it is possible to compare the two, the flush on Slack-ma-Girdle is a brighter red than Woodbine. Both varieties are ready at the same time in early November, but fruit will hang on the trees until January.

Size: Medium to large, 45–60mm.
Shape: Oblate; often lop-sided, round with slight ribs.
Stem: Thick stub, within or projecting slightly from a narrow, deep basin; basin in king fruits broad and shallow.
Eye: Basin broad, deep, irregular, bumpy, tending to crowned; calyx usually open, sepals free.
Skin: Pale green; smooth; lenticels often russeted dots.
Flush: Always 50–80%; pinkish-mauve diffuse, distinctly striped or flecked bright red.
Flesh: Sweet often with some astringency in the skin; pale greenish; chewy.
Core: Relatively small, slightly proximal; tube a deep cone sometimes open to core.
Juice: SG 1052; acidity 0.24%; tannin 0.14%.
Cider: Slack-ma-Girdle cider is very rich and full bodied with a good aroma and flavour. It is pleasant alone although somewhat sweet, so is better blended with a brisker cider.

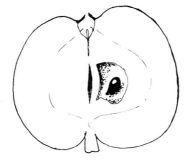

SOMERSET
Mid Season Sharp
Synonym: White Wine.

This variety was first recorded in 1831 and is described by Hogg simply as 'a culinary apple'. Somerset still occurs quite frequently as single large trees in old orchards in the Glastonbury to Shepton Mallet area. The variety called Somerset Lasting growing in the Brogdale Collection is a different apple.

Trees are often large and spreading and often stand alone in old orchards. It has all the attributes of a good general purpose apple; sweet and crisp, ready for eating in October and keeping well until February. It has an interesting flavour, pleasantly sharp, clean, refreshing and cidery. The fruits are large pale yellow, conical with a broad base and just a sprinkling of light pinkish-orange flush on the nose.

Size: Large to very large, more than 60mm.
Shape: Conical, broad rounded base and nose; slightly angular.
Stem: Very woody, sometimes green, usually within the cavity; basin medium, deep.
Eye: Basin small, narrow, slightly crowned, somewhat unevenly furrowed; calyx slightly open; sepals short, upright, often green.
Skin: Pale primrose or butter yellow; smooth, turning greasy with ripeness; russet in stem cavity, occasionally streaked and netted on nose and cheek; lenticels often small dots, sometimes large and red; scab susceptible.
Flush: Usually a trace to 30%; pink speckled with brown-orange dots and spots.
Flesh: Mild sharp with high sugar; sweet with clean refreshing flavour; firm crisp, melting; yellowish.
Core: Medium, slightly proximal, axile and slightly open, sometimes open towards tube; tube a small cone; stamens median.
Juice: Sharp; high sugar and high acid; pleasant flavour.
Cider: No cider-maker's notes found. Somerset on its own would probably make a rather thin cider but would be a pleasant addition to an orchard blend.

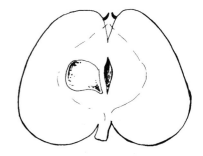

SOMERSET REDSTREAK
Early Bittersweet

Said to be an old variety from south east Somerset. Somerset Redstreak shares some characteristics with the bittersharps from the Lambrook area, such as Lambrook Pippin and Porter's Perfection. Unlike these, its fruits are a generous size, bittersweet and early. Somerset Redstreak may be less common in old standard orchards but it has been planted extensively since the 1970s. It has proved to be a useful, if biennial, early harvesting variety, and now occurs frequently in bush orchards in all the cider growing counties. The variety has gained sufficient recent popularity to be propagated as a standard for gapping-up old orchards.

Moderately vigorous trees with numerous primary lateral branches, but lack good centre leader dominance. Somerset Redstreak is predictably biennial in its cropping habit and makes a rather shapeless bush tree if left to its own devices. In its exuberance it often over-crops so heavily, and its wood is so brittle, that branches break under the strain. But such is its vitality that it constantly throws up new branches to replace the broken ones. Flowering is mid-season in early May. It is slightly susceptible to mildew, sawfly and brown rot but not scab.

The attractive shiny red apples are medium sized and conical. They mature early at the end of September and drop freely in early October, but the fallen fruits are quick to deteriorate if not collected promptly.

Size: Medium to large, 50 to more than 60mm.
Shape: Flattened conical, base rounded; regular; occasional fused fruits are produced.
Stem: Thick, fleshy, within or occasionally projecting slightly from a medium sized, fairly deep basin.
Eye: Basin usually broad, deep and slightly bumpy; calyx usually more or less open; sepals short.
Skin: Greenish-yellow; smooth, greasy or waxy, even sticky; russet is never more than slight in the stem basin; lenticels inconspicuous.
Flush: Always more than 75%; bright red, flecked and slightly striped darker red, spreading from eye, less round stem end.
Flesh: Sweet with astringency; juicy; white; chewy.
Core: Slightly open; seeds numerous, fat and round; tube a broad cone and short funnel.
Juice: SG 1050; acidity 0.19%; tannin 0.35%.
Cider: Can make a pleasant single variety cider, medium bittersweet with soft tannin. Often best when blended with several sharper varieties.

SOPS IN WINE
Dual Purpose
Synonyms: Sapson, Sapsovine etc.

Sops in Wine was described by Hogg as 'A very ancient (seventeenth century?) English culinary and cider apple, perhaps more singular than useful.' Bunyard says, 'There are many red fleshed apples to which this name is applied . . . It is of no particular merit.' However, it deserves a place here because it was at one time a common apple in West Country orchards and, at least in the nineteenth century, it undoubtedly made much cider.

Trees are vigorous and spreading, but it is said to be an excellent bearer. The fruits of the 'true' Sops in Wine are quite rounded and covered in a dark crimson flush. The flesh is white stained with red as if soaked in wine. It is sweet and juicy, only mildly sharp and has quite a pleasant flavour. Apples should be ripe by early to mid October.

Size: Medium to large, 50 to more than 60mm.
Shape: Rounded cylindrical, broad nose and rounded base; lopsided, tending to ribbed.
Stem: Woody; within or projecting slightly from a small but deep cavity.
Eye: Basin small, shallow even slight, tending to crowned; calyx open, sepals short.
Skin: Yellow; smooth, waxy; lenticels with pale surround; some scab.
Flush: Always present, often completely covered, dark red diffuse, slight stripes.
Flesh: Rather non-descript dessert, pleasant sweet, very mild sharp; melting; white with much reddening below skin and red vascular strands.
Core: Large, median, open; tube large, deep, U-shaped or deep funnel.
Juice: SG 1065; acidity 0.19%; tannin 0.13%.
Cider: No cider-maker's comments found but this variety is unlikely to be useful on its own.

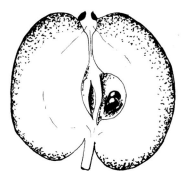

STABLE JERSEY
Late Full Bittersweet

This is a typical Somerset 'jersey' with a full bittersweet taste. Propagation material was brought to Long Ashton in 1987 for a clean-up and virus elimination. After that there were limited plantings in the 1980s by Showerings Cider Company, but this variety is quite frequent in old orchards from Shepton Mallet to Glastonbury. It has been propagated more recently as standard trees but it has not been adopted for bush orchard planting although it could have some potential as a late bittersweet.

Stable Jersey is said to be prone to canker. Trees are upright and spreading with rather unmanageable vigorous branches. It is a tip-bearer and flowers in mid May. The apples are bright red and gold striped, a rather waisted conical shape, and have a stub of a stem. They mature from mid October to early November.

Size: Medium to large, 45-60mm.
Shape: Conical, waisted; usually rounded with a trace of ribbing.
Stem: Thick, fleshy stub, usually within or projecting slightly from a slight or narrow basin.
Eye: Basin small but well defined, sometimes bumpy and irregularly beaded; calyx closed or sometimes slightly open; sepals green at base.
Skin: Pale golden yellow, slightly silvered; smooth, greasy; russet in stem cavity, occasional patches elsewhere.
Flush: Always more than 75%, often complete; heavy bright red strongly striped dark crimson.
Flesh: Full bittersweet; dry, chewy; greenish, browning rapidly.
Core: Median, small, closed; tube a fairly large cone.
Juice: SG 1058; acidity 0.25%, tannin 0.28%.
Cider: Stable Jersey makes a full flavoured cider but with a very hard tannin character. Useful for blending and extending.

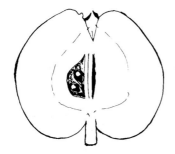

STEMBRIDGE CLUSTERS
Mid Season Bittersharp
Synonyms: Porter's Sheep's Nose, Sam Duck's Clusters/Perfection, possibly also Cluster Jersey.

Stembridge Clusters is a typical 'jersey' to look at, a rounded conical, striped apple with a long stem, but unusually for a 'jersey' this one is mild bittersharp. It may possibly have arisen as the result of a cross between a bittersweet 'jersey' and one of the Somerset bittersharps such as Lambrook Pippin. It was a protégé of Mr Sam Duck of Stembridge, who first called it his Perfection. Several old trees still stand in his orchard on Burrow Hill today. It was introduced for Taunton Cider in 1957, by the orcharding manager, John Stuckey of Stembridge, when it was almost certainly renamed Stembridge Clusters. In the 1970s it was widely planted in small quantities in bush orchards for Taunton Cider, but it is not popular because of its disease susceptibility. It is very inclined to scab, canker and blossom wilt, a disease which can almost wipe out the crop if left untreated.

True to its name it carries its fruit in clusters of up to five, and so has a strong tendency to crop biennially like many other old varieties. Moderate spurring develops with age. Bush trees are strong and spreading with much unruly vigour. The variety flowers in late May and the apples are ready for harvest by mid to late October. They are quite distinctive, yellow with scant but distinct bright red stripes and a long stem.

Size: Small to medium, 40-55mm.
Shape: Conical, sometimes conical-cylindrical; rounded and regular.
Stem: Woody, projecting distinctly from a slight basin.
Eye: Basin slight or small, often beaded or puckered; calyx open or closed, sepals upright, long.
Skin: Greenish-yellow; smooth and dry.
Flush: Usually about 30% but up to 65%; scant but distinct bright red stripes, a little orange diffuse flush but ground colour predominates.
Flesh: Sharp with mild astringency; greenish; juicy and chewy.
Core: Median, axile; tube a broad deep funnel.
Juice: SG 1050; acidity 0.50%; tannin 0.14%.
Cider: This variety was introduced after testing had finished at Long Ashton but its taste suggests that it would make a pleasantly flavoured, slightly thin, sharp cider.

STEMBRIDGE JERSEY
Late Mid Season Medium Bittersweet

This is a small Somerset 'jersey' apple, a useful bittersweet variety that first came to Long Ashton in 1947, sent in by Mr Stuckey of Stembridge, under the new name of Stembridge Jersey. It was submitted to the 1957 Long Ashton trials by his son John Stuckey, then Orchard Manager for Taunton Cider Company, and has subsequently found its way into many of the bush orchards that were planted to supply the Company in the 1970s.

Stembridge Jersey makes a medium to large, spreading tree which is quick growing and early into cropping but soon becomes biennial. It is not entirely suitable for bush orchards since it does tend to suffer from scab, severely on occasions. It flowers in mid May.

Stembridge Jersey apples are small, rather too small for economical machine harvesting in bush orchards. They are typical 'jersey' shape, flattened conical with a broad nose, and red and green stripes. They have unusually long stems. They mature from mid to late October but tend to drop over a long period as they ripen.

Size: Small to medium, 40-55mm.
Shape: Flattened, rounded conical, rather shouldered; angular in section.
Stem: Thick, fleshy, long, often strigged and offset, projecting distinctly from a small, deep basin.
Eye: Basin absent or slight, slightly beaded and furrowed; calyx closed, sepals short.
Skin: Greenish yellow; smooth, dry; lenticels often large and russeted with a pale surround; scab susceptible.
Flush: Usually a trace, sometimes up to 50%, pinkish, slightly striped with dark crimson.
Flesh: Medium bittersweet; greenish, browning rapidly, chewy.
Core: Median, open and large; tube fairly large cone, sometimes extending to core as a fine tube.
Juice: SG 1052; acidity 0.18%; tannin 0.24 - 0.50%.
Cider: This variety was introduced after cider trials had ceased at Long Ashton but its taste suggests that it would make a fair quality bittersweet cider with a typical Somerset character.

STOKE RED
Late Bittersharp
Synonyms: Neverblight, Stoke Redstripe.

Stoke Red came into prominence after 1926, when Long Ashton records and descriptions taken from trees growing at Rodney Stoke showed that it cropped heavily and consistently. As it was un-named, it was called Stoke Red. Subsequently older trees were found in the Wedmore area where it was known by the common name of Neverblight, after its robust reputation for resistance to pests and diseases. This is probably the location where the variety actually originated. From 1930 on, it was commonly included in trial orchards in all the cider growing counties, but it is more frequently found in Somerset. It is one of the parents of the widely planted early variety, Ashton Bitter.

Unfortunately Stoke Red has a poor natural tree shape. As a standard tree it is medium sized with a compact head formed of numerous small, twiggy branches. On a dwarfing rootstock it forms a neat bush with numerous branches but no centre leader. It is still fairly resistant to scab and mildew. Even as a bush it is slow to come into cropping and will invariably become biennial, but its crops are good. Flowering time is late May. Its main disadvantage as a bush tree is the small size of its fruit which matures fairly late, 3rd week November. It is quite easy to identify as small, flattened spherical and striped dark red.

Size: Small, less than 40-45mm.
Shape: Flattened spherical, rarely flattened conical; regular.
Stem: Variable; within cavity or projecting slightly from a slight or shallow stem basin.
Eye: Basin well defined, shallow, sometimes deep, regular, smooth, sometimes pubescent at the base; calyx closed, sepals very pubescent.
Skin: Yellow or greenish-yellow; smooth; slightly waxy; little scab; russet usually only in stem basin; lenticels usually inconspicuous.
Flush: Usually more than 75%, frequently complete; striped dark red.
Flesh: Sharp usually with some astringency; white, sometimes slightly reddened; soft, very juicy.
Core: Median or slightly proximal, axile usually open, loculi small; seeds numerous; tube a deep cone, sometimes a funnel; styles very pubescent.
Juice: SG 1052; acidity 0.64%; tannin 0.31%.
Cider: Stoke Red can produce an excellent, balanced, bittersharp juice which makes a very good, distinguished single variety cider with a pleasant fruity aroma, second only to Kingston Black and sometimes preferred. Fermentation can be slow.

STUBBARD
Very Early Dual Purpose
Synonyms: Stibbert, Summer Stibbert.

Described by Hogg as a very popular apple in the West of England, especially in Cornwall, Devon and Somerset, Stubbard or Stibbert is an early kitchen apple which comes into use from the middle of August. It is clearly a very old variety (pre-seventeenth century), reputed to root freely from cuttings, a sure sign of antiquity dating back to the early days of horticultural techniques. Comparison of Stubbard fruit with those of the wild apple *Malus sylvestris* shows how close this variety is to its origins. The Stubbard fruit in the illustration came from the cider orchard belonging to Mr Warren, cider maker of Netherbury, Dorset.

Stubbard trees are quite vigorous and flower in late April or early May. The fruit is distinctly boxy and ribbed, and the skin is pale yellow, faintly flushed with pink. Although the flesh is soft and juicy, it is well flavoured. Maturing early September.

Size: Medium to large, 45-60mm.
Shape: Cylindrical tending to conical with a nose; heavily ribbed from base to apex, irregular, angular and lop-sided.
Stem: Thick, fleshy, sometimes strigged; projecting distinctly from a narrow, deep basin.
Eye: Basin shallow, irregular, furrowed; calyx open.
Skin: Yellow; smooth and dry; occasionally slight russet dots.
Flush: None or very slight diffuse pinkish-brown.
Flesh: Sharp; white or cream; melting and juicy.
Core: Fairly large.
Juice: SG 1043; acidity 0.83%; tannin 0.17%.
Cider: No cider-maker's records found. As a very early maturing apple, Stubbard might be included with the first-early cider making of the season, when it would contribute a useful sharpness and some sugar.

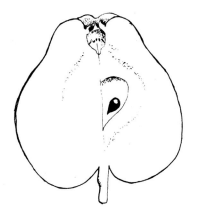

SWEET ALFORD
Late Mild Bittersweet

A well known and widely planted variety which originated in Devon, where it has a reputation for good cropping. It occurs in Somerset as mature trees, which have performed with disappointing results. Standard trees are large and slightly spreading, with characteristic forked twigs due to its tip-bearing habit. Many bush trees under the name, Sweet Alford, planted by Taunton Cider Company, are in fact another variety called Le Bret. This may have occurred during propagation at Long Ashton for the virus-free mother tree orchard. Sweet Alford seems to be very susceptible to scab.

Sweet Alford fruits have a waxy yellow skin often with a diffuse flush associated with damage or bruising. They are distinguished from Le Bret by their smaller size and by their long, thin stems. This variety flowers in mid May and the fruit matures in the first part of November.

Size: Medium, 45-55mm.
Shape: Flattened conical.
Stem: Thin, woody; projecting considerably from a pronounced, deep basin.
Eye: Basin shallow, puckered; calyx slightly open, sepals large, reflexed, upright.
Skin: Yellow, sometimes greenish-yellow; smooth, waxy; russet sometimes a thin network; scab susceptible.
Flush: Frequent, covering less than a third, slight; diffuse pink-orange.
Flesh: Sweet, no astringency; white, slightly crisp.
Core: Slightly distal, axile, open; tube a deep cone or funnel.
Juice: SG 1052; acidity 0.22%; tannin 0.15%.
Cider: Sweet, sometimes mild bittersweet; good quality.

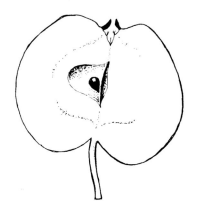

SWEET COPPIN
Late Mid Season Sweet

An old Devon variety, found throughout Somerset as middle aged trees, and in some of the trial orchards. More recently it has been propagated by Bulmers as standard trees and has now found its way into many renovated orchards. It is only rarely used as a bush tree in this county.

Mature trees are fairly easy to recognise, both standard and bush, from the large, rounded head of thin whippy, twiggy growth. In the dormant season, the bark on current year's shoot growth has a distinctive golden sheen. As bush trees Sweet Coppin can crop quite regularly when persuaded to, but fruit is late to mature, ready towards the end of October and into November. Flowering time is mid season. Rather susceptible to mildew.

The apples are basically conical in shape and frequently large on lightly cropping trees, but there are often many king fruits which are much more cylindrical. The skin is a pale yellow usually with a patch of orange, or mauvish flush.

Size: Medium, often large, 50 to more than 60mm.
Shape: Basically conical, sometimes flattened spherical, regular; king fruits cylindrical often irregular.
Stem: Woody, usually projecting slightly from a wide, shallow basin.
Eye: Basin well defined, wide, shallow, smooth; calyx slightly open, sepals narrow, often free.
Skin: Yellow to greenish-yellow; dry; russet usually light, sometimes spreading as network on cheek; lenticels conspicuous, sometimes large and irregular, some surrounded by a small circle of red, lenticel spot common.
Flush: Usually just a patch of diffuse orange-pink, occasionally flecked red.
Flesh: Sweet with no astringency; white, soft.
Core: Median, abaxile, sometimes only open loculi.
Juice: SG 1052; acidity 0.20%; tannin 0.14%.
Cider: Pure sweet, occasionally very mild bittersweet.

SWEET PETHYRE
Late Sweet

There is some confusion over the true identity of this variety, in truth, there are two Pethyres. Most of the Long Ashton cider house records refer to fruit brought in from orchards in Monmouth, many of them from the village of Perthyre itself. Their true identity was given as Perthyre, Belle Norman or Handsome Norman, a bell-shaped, dark green apple. The genuine Somerset variety, spelt Pethyre, is nearer a pure sweet. It attracted quite a bit of attention in the 1920s because the quality of its cider was sometimes judged as excellent. It probably came originally from east Somerset, the Glastonbury to Shepton Mallet locality, since it is still found there and resembles other local varieties. It might just have been high-jacked, then renamed on discovery as a Monmouth variety.

Sweet Pethyre trees in Somerset are large and disease free, though of medium vigour. Flowering is mid season. The apples, ready towards the end of October, are distinctive. They are quite large, dirty looking green, angular fruits with a brown tip to the nose. But their appearance belies their taste. They are sweet and meltingly juicy.

Size: Large to very large, more than 60mm.
Shape: Conical, tending to cylindrical, waisted, nose elongated, base rounded; angular, distinctly ribbed.
Stem: Short, within a medium to large, deep basin.
Eye: Basin small, well defined, narrow, deep, crowned, occasionally beaded, distinctly russeted; calyx more or less open, sepals long, upright, reflexed.
Skin: Bright green to yellow-green; smooth; slightly waxy; russet often heavy and spreading in network.
Flush: Frequent, a trace to 30%; pinkish-orange diffuse only.
Flesh: Sweet with a trace of tannin; yellowish, vascular strands green; melting.
Core: Large and open; tube medium, conical.
Juice: SG 1045; acidity 0.20%; tannin 0.14%.
Cider: Pethyre's sweet, slightly astringent juice produces a mild bittersweet cider of variable quality, sometimes excellent.

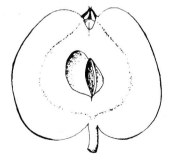

TAYLOR'S SWEET
Mid Season Sweet
Synonym: Taylor's Seedling.

This old variety, sometimes incorrectly called Taylor's Bitter, was originally propagated at Porter's Nursery near South Petherton, in the late nineteenth century. Although it is a sweet apple with little tannin in the juice, it was planted in many new bush cider orchards throughout the counties to act as a pollinator for the more valued, early flowering variety, Tremlett's Bitter.

Taylor's Sweet is a true tip bearer. Each fruit cluster produces two shoots which in turn produce two others. Because of this curious dichotomous branching habit, it forms a distinctive weeping tree. It is quite vigorous and produces few useful primary branches. As a bush tree it is difficult to maintain a good centre leader and spurring is very poor. It is not precocious and will slowly go biennial. Leaves of this variety are distinctively grey, with a pale underside. Flowering time is late April, early May and the cream coloured blossom is particularly attractive.

The apples which are often held in multiple clusters, are tall and distinctly but sparsely striped red and green. They fall early to mid October and are fairly firm.

Size: Large, 55-60mm.
Shape: Cylindrical tending to conical; oval in cross section.
Stem: Woody, projecting distinctly; basin medium, narrow and deep.
Eye: Basin slight, shallow, irregular; calyx often open, sepals reflexed, long.
Skin: Pale yellow-green; smooth, dry; russet often in stem cavity.
Flush: Always 30% or less, light red diffuse, strongly flecked and striped crimson.
Flesh: Sweet; chewy, firm; white, browning rapidly.
Core: Median; often with few seeds; tube a large cone, broad and deep; stamens distal; styles often fleshy.
Juice: SG 1053; acidity 0.18%; tannin 0.15%.
Cider: Taylor's Seedling produces a light to medium cider with good flavour and aroma but rather coarse, lacking character and quality. Useful for blending.

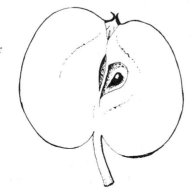

TEN COMMANDMENTS
Dual purpose apple

This well known apple frequently occurs in farm orchards throughout the West Country and also in Hereford. It gets its name from the reddened vascular strands in the flesh which show up as ten red spots when the fruit is cut in half. Sometimes in fruit from old orchards these vascular strands are not coloured, especially if the trees are overgrown and the orchard is dark so that the fruit gets little sunlight. There seem to be many descriptions and many variations of this variety, some of them possibly just look-alike seedlings that go under the same name. The apples of true Ten Commandments are an eye-catching beetroot red often with conspicuous light coloured dots.

Trees are moderately vigorous. Their blossom is attractive in early May. Ten Commandments is a dual purpose apple, sub-acid, useful for eating, cooking or putting in with the cider. The red colour of the juice and flesh might just tint the cider pink if there was a sufficient quantity of them in the blend. Ready for harvest in early October.

Size: Medium, 45-55mm.
Shape: Rather oblate or flattened conical; rounded tending to angular.
Stem: A short thick stub within the cavity; basin small but fairly deep.
Eye: Basin medium, smooth and regular; sepals wide open, often short.
Skin: Yellow; smooth, dry or slightly waxy with age; russet usually confined to stem basin; lenticels very conspicuous, large, russeted.
Flush: Often complete, strongly diffuse or slightly striped with dark, beetroot red, sometimes slightly striped bright red.
Flesh: Sharp, sub-acid; melting; white, reddened under the skin, often with red vascular strands.
Core: Small, median; tube a very small cone; seeds few.
Juice: SG 1055; acidity 0.18%; tannin 0.13%; nitrogen 15.2mg/100mg (average 5-10mg/100mg).
Cider: Ten Commandments is unlikely to make a good cider alone, but it might be an intriguing and attractive colour. Best blended with bittersweet varieties. Nitrogen may be high in some samples and fermentation will be accelerated.

TOMMY RODFORD
Late Bittersweet
Synonyms: Rodford, more recently Black Dabinett.

Tommy Rodford apples were recorded at the Bath and West Show in 1897, from Kingsbury Episcopi in central Somerset, and some trees were recently found still standing in an old orchard in the village. This apple is probably a sport or a seedling of the true Dabinett but it is rather more robust. In the mid 1980s it was thought that it might have some potential for bush orchards and so was propagated on a small scale. Young trees are flourishing under the name Black Dabinett in some recent trials orchards, but it is rather late maturing and for that reason, it is unlikely to become fashionable at the present time. But its fruit has excellent vintage quality and it is a variety that deserves to be more widely planted.

Tommy Rodford trees are vigorous and spreading but well spurred. The variety should crop well as bush trees. Flowering is late mid season with Dabinett and Chisel Jersey.

The fruit of Tommy Rodford is a similar shape to the true Dabinett but it matures a bit later, well into November. It can be distinguished from it by its darker, purple-brown flush often covered with an attractive network of russet and dots, and by the curious whitish patches which occur on some fruits. Churchill is another similar variety from the same locality.

Size:	Medium, 45-55mm.
Shape:	Conical tending to oblate; rounded, sometimes angular.
Stem:	Often off-set, projects distinctly, from a deep, often slightly furrowed basin; just a stub in king fruits.
Eye:	Basin small, slightly furrowed; calyx closed.
Skin:	Dark green, with lighter patches; dry; russet usually in distinctive spreading network.
Flush:	Always, 50% to nearly complete, diffuse and slightly flecked dark purple-red.
Flesh:	Bittersweet; dry, chewy; strongly greenish, vascular strands green.
Core:	Tube medium conical.
Juice:	SG 1048; acidity 0.23%; tannin 0.28%.
Cider:	Tommy Rodford cider was recorded in 1908 as 'a sweet, fairly full flavoured cider of pleasant taste and aroma.' Although it could be used alone, it was described as too bitter, and best for blending.

TOM PUTT
Early Dual purpose
Synonyms: Coalbrook, Marrowbone, Ploughman and many others.

Tom Putt is an eighteenth century variety which has now become rather variable. It is arguable whether it is a native of Devon, Dorset or of Somerset, since it was either raised by the Reverend Thomas Putt (1757-1844), rector of Trent, which is now in Dorset but was formerly in Somerset, or by his uncle, Tom Putt who lived near Honiton in Devon. It may have been him who brought it to Trent, to his nephew's garden. It is still widely distributed as a dual purpose apple all over the West Country. Always popular for gardens and home orchards, it is sometimes referred to as the Cottage Apple. Tom Putt has been quoted as 'A rosy apple that grew in every garden and every orchard.'

Tom Putt trees are vigorous and spreading. They have remarkable powers of rejuvenation even in old age, often throwing out new, vigorous branches from the base or even from the remains of a stump. It is an early flowering variety and because of this, seems to be prone to apple sawfly.

Tom Putt fruits are full of character, broadly conical, rather knobbly and irregular, and more or less covered with a striped and flecked, bright red flush. Apples begin to drop in August, often because of codling moth which seem to be common, and tend to rot quickly. The flesh is soft and sharp and tastes good cooked. There are also Red and White Tom Putts, which are similar in all other respects.

Size:	Large, 55 to more than 60mm.
Shape:	Flattened conical, broad base, narrow nose; strongly ribbed, irregular.
Stem:	Short, within or protruding slightly from a medium, narrow basin.
Eye:	Basin deep, ribbed or crowned, irregular; calyx open, sepals short, upright.
Skin:	Greenish yellow; shiny, waxy; very little russet; scab susceptible.
Flush:	Rather variable, always more than 75%, distinctly striped and flecked, bright crimson over red diffuse. Red Tom Putt, a sport with heavy red diffuse flush and no stripes.
Flesh:	Sub acid; soft; yellowish.
Core:	Large, axile, open; tube short, wide, conical.
Juice:	SG 1052; acidity 0.65%, tannin 0.13%.
Cider:	Tom Putt, a typical dual purpose apple, is a mild sharp and makes a somewhat thin, dry and sharp cider. But its flavour is clean and pleasant and it usually improves after keeping a while.

TREMLETT'S BITTER
Early Bittersweet

A popular Devon variety which is commonly found throughout all the cider growing counties in bush and standard orchards planted since the 1950s. Although very biennial in its cropping, Tremlett's can produce huge crops of smallish fruit. It is a useful early variety, maturing in the first half of October. It has the disadvantage of flowering very early, often in late April, when it is at risk of being caught by late frosts. Although self-sterile and needing a pollinator like Taylor's Seedling, it is a useful pollinator for other early varieties.

Mature standard trees are medium sized with a spreading habit. Bush trees are somewhat difficult to manage, being full of vigour they tend to throw out branches in all directions, forming a dense mass around the centre leader. It is a very scab susceptible variety and, when both the fruit and leaves are affected, often defoliated. Tremlett's Bitter apples are strikingly bright red, elongated conical with a rather pointed nose.

Size:	Medium, 45-55mm.
Shape:	Conical tending to elongated; base round, nose pointed.
Stem:	Woody, usually projecting slightly from a small, shallow basin.
Eye:	Basin small; calyx tightly closed, sepals long and reflexed, pubescent.
Skin:	Yellow, sometimes greenish; smooth and waxy; lenticels conspicuous, usually small but surrounded by a light patch; scab susceptible.
Flush:	Always more than two thirds, often complete, bright, mid red, slightly striped.
Flesh:	Sweet and astringent; white, woolly.
Core:	Slightly proximal, axile, open; tube a cone or funnel.
Juice:	SG 1052; acidity 0.27%; tannin 0.34%.
Cider:	Full bittersweet, hard and bitter tannin.

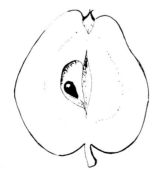

VALLIS APPLE
Mid Season Sharp
Synonyms: Black or Red Vallis, Redskins.

Although this variety looks similar to the true Kingston Black, it comes nowhere near the legendary 'KB' flavour and vintage quality. Its taste gives its identity away as soon as it is compared with Kingston Black's more balanced flavour, bittersharp with considerable acidity and tannin. Vallis is a pure sharp with little tannin and probably more closely related to Improved Kingston Black. It is often familiarly known as Redskins in North Somerset where it originated. This shiny red apple was attractive and palatable enough to be sold for an eating apple in Bristol Market at one time.

Trees are large, even very large, upright and spreading, with a full head of dark green leaves. It is described as a good cropper, better than true Kingston Black and less prone to scab and canker, but seems to be susceptible to sawfly. Flowering time is late May.

Vallis apples are rather variable in shape, but are usually round and regular, and quite distinctively flattened like a top. The fruits are quite large and more or less covered in a strong red flush, dark, often almost black in places. They are ready from mid to late October. There are some variations in different districts and there may be more than one variety.

Size:	Medium to large, 50 to more than 60mm.
Shape:	Variable, usually oblate, base and nose broad; sometimes more conical tending to waisted; basically regular but often lopsided, tending to angular.
Stem:	Thin, woody, projecting distinctly from a large, broad, deep basin.
Eye:	Basin medium, narrow, deep, furrowed or irregular, crowned or slightly beaded; calyx usually closed, sepals upright, long, broad, free.
Skin:	Yellow to yellow-green; smooth, greasy, very shiny; slight scab.
Flush:	Always more than 75% often almost complete; strong, bright cherry red to bright red diffuse, occasional patches almost black.
Flesh:	Sharp, sweet, dessert taste and texture; juicy, melting; greenish, often tinged with red under the skin.
Core:	Medium, slightly distal, open, abaxile; seeds often few; tube a broad cone open to core.
Juice:	SG 1056; acidity 0.70%; tannin 0.15%.
Cider:	Red Vallis was reported to make a pleasant, clean tasting but not outstanding cider. Fermentation may be rather rapid.

VILBERIE
Late Bittersweet

This is a French variety introduced by H.P. Bulmer in the late nineteenth century. It is not usually found as old standard trees in Somerset, but does occur as youngish replacement trees, and in a few bush orchards planted for Showering's and Taunton Cider Company in the early 1970s. It is normally found in association with Brown Snout, another late flowering and maturing variety.

Vilberie trees are very vigorous, open and spreading. It is difficult to maintain a good centre leader since it tends to go over to the leeward side. It is susceptible to leaf mildew and frequently gets fireblight because of its late flowering habit. Vilberie apples are rather flattened conical and green with a dull, brownish flush. Although they are not ready to harvest until well into November, they weigh heavily and produce good crops.

Size: Medium, 45-55mm.
Shape: Flattened conical; regular or slightly angular.
Stem: Long, usually projecting considerably from a narrow basin.
Eye: Basin small, puckered; calyx slightly open, sepals long and reflexed.
Skin: Dark green, waxy; russet slight in stem basin, occasionally spreading in patches.
Flush: Usually one - two thirds, diffuse spreading from the eye, brownish-red.
Flesh: Full bittersweet; greenish; chewy, hard.
Core: Median, axile, medium size; tube a broad cone.
Juice: SG 1062; acidity 0.23%; tannin 0.50%.
Cider: Sweet with full astringency; good quality.

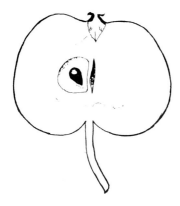

WEAR AND TEAR
Mid Season Dual Purpose
Synonyms: Glastonbury Wear and Tear, Bear and Tear.

There are still odd trees of Wear and Tear standing in old orchards round the Glastonbury area where it originated, even one or two on the Tor itself. It is aptly named from its habit of breaking under the weight of heavy crops, but it has the remarkable ability to rejuvenate itself, producing strong new limbs even in old age. This variety was first recorded in 1883, but it is probably very old.

Trees are tall, upright and spread with maturity. Some old trees are now showing signs of virus infection and their fruit is cracked and scarred and useless.

The apples are quite elongated conical with an irregular eye. The fruit stems are often distinctive, bulging and knobbly, and sometimes coloured pink. The flesh is often very sweet which masks some sharpness, and the texture is crisp like a dessert apple. Maturity mid October to early November.

Size: Medium, 45-55mm.
Shape: Elongated conical with a broad base; often disfigured with scab and virus infection.
Stem: Thick, woody, usually with a bulge at fruit end, projecting slightly, occasionally distinctly, sometimes coloured pink when flush is in stem basin; king fruits with very thick, fleshy stems; stem basin medium, conical, slightly ribbed.
Eye: Basin fairly deep, very puckered, ribbed; usually irregular through scab; calyx closed, sepals touching, overlapping, fairly long, reflexed at tips.
Skin: Yellowish green; smooth, slightly waxy; lenticels conspicuous in bruises on ripe fruit; very scab susceptible.
Flush: About 60%, diffuse dragon's blood red, sometimes flushed pinkish in stem basin.
Flesh: Heavy sweet; white, vascular strands green; dry; very soft dessert texture.
Core: Tending to proximal; tube distinctive, wide, deep, rectangular in section.
Juice: Heavy sweet.
Cider: No comments recorded but should make a good, rather thin sweet cider, so is probably best blended with other varieties with more character.

WHITE CLOSE PIPPIN
Medium Bittersweet
Synonym: Dry Close.

White Close Pippin is scarce in its native county of Somerset. Although mentioned at the Bath and West Show in 1898, the earliest records at Long Ashton were of fruit sent from Sutton Montis in 1907. It clearly has good vintage qualities. Standard trees may still be found in Devon but it occurs in other counties only occasionally in some experimental bush orchards that were planted in the 1930s. It has been referred to as Dry Close in South Petherton, but whether this is a misspelling or a misnomer, is hard to say.

White Close forms a medium sized tree with a spreading habit, quite vigorous. It is free spurring and has been described as forming a 'thistle top' head, with its pale, whitish foliage. Cropping is said to be variable, sometimes heavy, and it is slightly susceptible to scab. Flowering time is mid season in May.

The apples are pale green, almost white or creamy, sometimes heavily cracked and russeted. There is usually a patch of rosy-pink flush on the cheek. The prominent lenticels, surrounded by a green patch on immature fruit, are a distinctive feature. Maturing from mid October to November.

Size:	Medium, 55-60mm.
Shape:	Conical, nose flat; rather irregular; king fruit slightly elongated.
Stem:	Level with base, more usually projecting slightly or considerably; basin broad, deep.
Eye:	Basin small, smooth or slightly puckered; calyx more or less open or wide open, sepals upright, rather pubescent.
Skin:	Very pale greenish white or cream; smooth, dry; russet often spreading from stem basin and nose, frequently net-like on cheek; lenticels often russeted; fruit sometimes heavily cracked with scab.
Flush:	Usual; 25-50%; diffuse, slightly flecked or striped, rather pinkish orange.
Flesh:	Medium or mild bittersweet, tannin in skin; pale yellow; chewy texture.
Core:	Slightly open, loculi small; tube a funnel, often deep.
Juice:	SG 1050; acidity 0.18%; tannin 0.24%.
Cider:	White Close Pippin makes a rich and fruity cider with an excellent flavour and aroma. The tannin is mild, so it can be good alone or blended. Sugar content is often above average but fermentation is inclined to be slow.

WHITE JERSEY
Early Bittersweet

Still widely distributed in old farm orchards in Somerset, White Jersey was popular as a cider apple in the nineteenth century, and was listed by Lloyd for the Bath and West Society in 1895. More recently has been considered to have some promise as an early maturing variety for bush orchards. From the mid 1980s, it was often planted with Ashton Bitter, Ellis Bitter and Major although it has not enjoyed quite the same popularity as the others.

Although it will form a good centre leader shape without too much training, it is slow to get started. It makes up for this by being extremely precocious and heavy cropping. Young bush trees have moderate vigour but are well furnished with laterals. The growth is semi-spreading and spurring plentiful. It is easily trained as a centre leader. As a standard tree, White Jersey is only small or medium sized when mature, with a neat, compact head of many spurred branches. Susceptible to mildew. Flowering mid season in mid May, it is not suitable as a pollinator because it produces little pollen, but it seems to be self fertile.

Its fruit which falls freely in late September to early October is usually rather small, golden yellow without flush, and conical with a typical 'jersey' nose.

Size:	Small to medium, 45-55mm.
Shape:	Conical, base rounded; often rather lopsided, slightly angular.
Stem:	Fairly fleshy, thick, green, usually projecting slightly from a small, broad, shallow basin.
Eye:	Basin slight, or small and shallow, eye usually fairly smooth, sometimes slightly puckered; calyx closed.
Skin:	Primrose yellow; smooth; dry; russet often a flash in stem cavity, sometimes a net spreading from eye.
Flush:	Absent.
Flesh:	Medium to full bittersweet; juicy; chewy; pale yellowish.
Core:	Median, small; often few seeds; tube deep, narrow funnel.
Juice:	SG 1051; acidity 0.29%; tannin 0.26%.
Cider:	The good quality juice of White Jersey is sweet and astringent, producing a dry, rather bitter cider which is useful for extending.

WOODBINE
Late Sweet
Synonyms: Runaway, Rice's Jersey [Glastonbury district].

Found throughout Somerset, Devon and Dorset where it is still popular in traditional orchards, Woodbine is one of a group of similar apples, all vigorous trees with sweet tasting fruit producing cider with a curious woody after-taste. Northwood is a similar variety which often occurs in orchards in Devon and on the border with Somerset. Woodbine is often said to be the same as Slack-ma-Girdle. They are both distinct although it is sometimes only possible to tell them apart by looking at the tree habit. Woodbine forms an open tree with a few long, spreading limbs. Slack-ma-Girdle is more compact with numerous limbs. There is also an Improved Woodbine which looks similar to the parent, but is very susceptible to scab and has little to recommend it.

Woodbine is very fast growing and was often used as a stem and framework tree in the Glastonbury to Shepton Mallet area, were it is still known as Rice's Jersey. As for its other name, Runaway. Although it makes a useful if rather alternative flavoured cider, its effects on the digestive system have earned it a medicinal reputation!

Woodbine fruits are medium sized, flattened and two thirds covered with a distinctive rosy-red striped flush, speckled with small brown dots. It is very scab susceptible. Maturing mid-late October.

Size: Medium to large, 45 to more than 60mm.
Shape: Oblate; often lopsided, somewhat angular tending to ribbed.
Stem: Thick stub, sometimes strigged or with bulge at spur end, projecting slightly or within a rather deep basin.
Eye: Basin medium, often broad and deep; irregular tending to crowned, often deformed by scab; calyx open or closed, sepals often free, upright, green.
Skin: Green to yellow-green; smooth and dry; lenticels as small brown dots; scab susceptible.
Flush: Always, 25-75%; flecked and striped, pinkish-red to greyish-mauve.
Flesh: Sweet; chewy; greenish, vascular strands green.
Core: Median, open, usually large; tube a cone, sometimes open to core.
Juice: SG 1051; acidity 0.2%; tannin 0.12%.
Cider: Woodbine cider is rather lacking in character, but has a pleasant, curiously woody flavour. It is useful for blending. Fermentation is slow to medium.

YARLINGTON MILL
Late Mid Season Bittersweet

A genuine Somerset 'jersey' apple, it is said to have been discovered by a Mr Bartlett, born in 1898 in the village of Yarlington near North Cadbury, as a 'gribble' growing out of the wall by the water wheel of the mill. His grandfather planted it in the garden to use it as a stock but, when in due course it bore good, bittersweet apples that made a fair cider, it was kept and named Yarlington Mill. It was very likely propagated by Mr Harry Masters, a nurseryman in that area in the late nineteenth century. In the middle of the twentieth century it was reintroduced and used widely for head working unproductive varieties. Later, in the 1970s, it was chosen for many bush orchards planted by Taunton Cider Company, where it constitutes about 15% of the acreage. Yarlington Mill has proved to be very popular and is still propagated and planted enthusiastically, both as a bush and a standard tree. It grows in many areas of the West Country where it invariably performs reliably, but rather biennially, under widely different conditions.

A mature standard tree is medium sized with an upright habit which tends to become spreading. Its leaves are distinctively large, rounded and dark shiny green. Young bush trees have plentiful, sparingly spurred, much branching laterals, which droop under the crop. It is not an easy variety to maintain a good centre leader. Precocious and heavy cropping, if rather biennial, Yarlington Mill responds well to pruning and fruit thinning to keep its cropping more regular. It is moderately susceptible to scab on both leaves and fruit. Flowering time is early mid season, before Michelin.

Yarlington Mill fruit is a typical 'jersey' shape, often quite large, conical with a distinct nose and yellow with a pinkish flush. It is similar to Major but much later maturing. Its long stem distinguishes it from Harry Masters' Jersey, another similar variety. Maturity late October to early November.

Size: Medium to large, 50 to more than 60mm.
Shape: Conical, sometimes tending to cylindrical; base flat; nose distinct.
Stem: Projecting slightly, sometimes level with the base; basin wide, deep.
Eye: Basin rather small, puckered; calyx usually slightly open, sepals short.
Skin: Yellow or greenish-yellow; smooth; slightly waxy; russet usually confined to stem basin; lenticels inconspicuous; scab susceptible.
Flush: Usually; about 65%; slightly striped or flecked dark red with paler background.
Flesh: Sweet with some astringency; white, frequently reddened under flush; slightly crisp.

Core: Slightly proximal, axile; loculi sometimes open; seeds numerous; tube conical.
Juice: SG 1052; acidity 0.22%; tannin 0.32%.
Cider: Yarlington Mill's medium bittersweet juice is good and makes a pleasant tasting cider with an agreeable aroma.

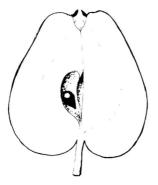

YELLOW REDSTREAK
Late Mild Bittersharp

Yellow Redstreak is probably a very old variety. It was described in 1886, by Hogg in *Apples and Pears as Vintage Fruits*, as 'a high sugar variety valuable for mixing with other more astringent varieties for cider making'. It was collected for the Whetons Museum Orchard in Hereford in 1964 from an old orchard in Stembridge, Somerset. Later, in the 1980s, it was propagated from that material for a bush orchard trial at Long Ashton. It was often used as a rootstock and stem builder in Somerset in the past because it is vigorous and rather upright. It also grows well from seed to produce a uniform crop of young trees, very useful for grafting. Yellow Redstreak is still sometimes found as trees where the scion variety has failed with age, but it was also planted as a variety in its own right.

Bush trees are strong growing, stiff and upright with much bare wood; not an ideal habit. The fruits which mature late in October, are broadly flattened conical. The skin is light striped and streaked with red, but the yellow skin colour predominates.

Size: Medium to large, 45 to more than 60mm.
Shape: Flattened conical, base rounded; lopsided, angular, ribbed.
Stem: Slender, projecting distinctly; stem basin narrow, deep.
Eye: Basin small, narrow, deep, furrowed, sometimes crowned, beaded; calyx more or less closed, sepals short, upright.
Skin: Pale yellow; smooth; becoming greasy with ripeness.
Flush: Usually 30-60%; striped and flecked bright scarlet, a little pink diffuse flush beneath.
Flesh: Sharp with some tannin; yellowish; cider texture.
Core: Smallish, median, abaxile, open; tube a large cone.
Juice: Mild bittersharp.
Cider: No cider-maker's comments found, but Yellow Redstreak probably makes an indifferent cider, and is likely to be a greater asset as a framework tree.

YEOVIL SOUR

Late Medium Sharp
Synonym: Sour Cadbury.

Yeovil Sour was first mentioned as a bittersharp in the *History of Somerset* in 1830. Fruit came to Long Ashton early in the twentieth century, called Yeovil Sour from Martock and Sour Cadbury from Woolston in the south west corner of Somerset, not far from Yeovil. Some trees were planted soon after at Long Ashton, and their progress and the quality of their cider were tested from 1914 to the early 1920s. The trees were still there at Long Ashton as late as 1952. Sadly, there is no longer any trace of this variety although it was recorded by Prof. Barker in his list of Vintage varieties recommended for planting.

Yeovil Sour trees are moderately vigorous, upright and spreading. Flowering is mid-season to late May and crops were recorded as heavy but biennial.

Yeovil Sour is a late maturing apple, not ready until November. Its smallish conical fruit with its pinkish flushed cheek, looks similar to Cadbury from which it is distinguished by its taste. Cadbury, a mild bittersweet, has more pronounced tannin than Yeovil Sour, a mild sharp.

Size: Small to medium, 40-55mm.
Shape: Flattened conical, base broad and flat, nose broad; regular, tending to ribbed.
Stem: Very short; within a small shallow basin.
Eye: Basin small, smooth, regular; calyx usually closed, often slightly open.
Skin: Pale yellow; rough, dry; covered with a network of fine patchy russet especially associated with lenticels.
Flush: Usual; less than 50%; diffuse pinkish-orange.
Flesh: Sharp.
Juice: SG 1052; acidity 0.55%; tannin 0.15%.
Cider: Yeovil Sour cider has been described as medium brisk with an attractive character in favourable seasons, but usually best blended. It is medium sharp and the sugar content is often above average.

PART 3

IDENTIFICATION OF CIDER APPLES

The development of a discriminating palate is a prerequisite for the orchard detective. The first and most important step towards identifying a cider apple is to taste it. They can all be loosely grouped into any one of the four taste categories as bittersweets or pure sweets, bittersharps or sharps, so it is essential to be able to detect the presence of tannin by its bitterness or astringency. Initially some people find it quite difficult to distinguish between bitter and acid tastes, but once the tangy citric taste of a pure sharp cider apple has been experienced, it is easy to distinguish it from the warmer, furry, tea taste of a good bittersweet. Both are a surprise to the novice palate but once acquired, the tastes are unexpectedly addictive. With practice it soon becomes possible to differentiate between a mouth-drawing sensation of astringency, and a more tongue-furring bitter taste. Soon it will also be clear why a true sharp apple has a more valuable flavour for cider-making than a culinary tasting dual purpose apple.

SEASON: Although the time when the fruit is ready for harvesting varies greatly from year to year, there are three broad maturity seasons for cider apples; *Early*, from the end of September until early October; *Mid season*, ready sometime in October; and *Late*, not ready until November.

VISUAL CHARACTERS: The next move is to study the least variable visual characters, the most stable of which are the general shape and the stem. To make an accurate identification, not less than 20 fruits should be selected, preferably sampled randomly when they are ripe and falling freely.

SHAPE: Cider apples fall into six basic shapes, as shown in the figure opposite. Some typical examples are: *Round*; Stoke Red, Sharpshooter: *Oblate*; Vallis Apple, Improved Kingston Black: *Cylindrical*; Dunkerton's Late, Silver Cup: *Conical*; this includes most of the 'jerseys': *Flattened conical*; Pennard Bitter, Chisel Jersey: *Elongated conical*; Broad Leaved Jersey.

Many varieties may lie somewhere in between, such as Cap of Liberty which is between conical and cylindrical. Usually the king fruits, the first fruits to set in the cluster, are a different shape from the later fruits. Kingston Black often has many of both. The king fruits are cylindrical and the rest are flattened conical, appearing almost like two different varieties.

The fruit base is an important character. A wide base such as found in Yarlington Mill is a constant feature in this variety. Many bittersweet 'jerseys' are 'waisted' with a distinct constricted nose. Fused fruits are sometimes found on several varieties but are frequent in Porter's Perfection.

STEM AND STEM BASIN: The stem length varies only slightly within a variety and is a good diagnostic feature. The stem basin has to be judged in relation to the overall size of the fruit, thus similar dimensions may be called small in large fruits but large in small ones. An irregular stem basin, flattened on one side, occurs in Backwell Red.

EYE BASIN AND CALYX: Like the stem basin, the size of the eye basin need to be judged in relation to the size of the fruit. Puckering and ribbing are important and usually constant, as is beading round the eye. The calyx is more variable, but sometimes the sepals are a

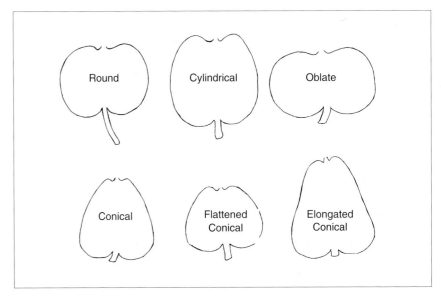

Round   Cylindrical   Oblate

Conical   Flattened Conical   Elongated Conical

useful feature. They may be upright around an open eye, or long, green and reflexed.

SKIN: Five characters are important; the presence or absence of *wax*, but this depends on the ripeness of the fruit and whether or not it has been lying for a time in the grass; the position and quantity of *russet*, such as the distinct russet patch around the eye in Brown Snout which is instantly recognisable; the background colour of the *skin*; the type, colour and quantity of the *flush*; and the conspicuousness of the *lenticels*.

INTERNAL CHARACTERS: Such details as the core, the tube and the colour and texture of the flesh are more variable. An identification should not rely heavily on these factors, but use them to confirm the more stable evidence.

LIST OF VARIETIES DESCRIBED

BITTERSWEET
Ashton Bitter
Ashton Brown Jersey
Broadleaf Jersey
Brown Snout
Bulmers Norman
Burrow Hill Early
Cadbury
Camelot
Chisel Jersey
Churchill
Coat Jersey
Dabinett
Dove
Early Red Jersey
Ellis Bitter
Fillbarrel
Hangdown
Harry Masters' Jersey
Improved Dove
Improved Hangdown
Major
Michelin
Norton Bitters
Pennard Bitter
Red Jersey
Royal Jersey
Silver Cup
Somerset Redstreak
Stable Jersey
Stembridge Jersey
Tommy Rodford
Tremlett's Bitter

Vilberie
White Close Pippin
White Jersey
Yarlington Mill

SHARP
Backwell Red
Brown's Apple
Cider Lady's Finger
Crimson King
Fair Maid of Taunton
Gin
Improved Kingston Black
Improved Lambrook Pippin
Langworthy
Neverblight
Somerset
Vallis Apple
Yeovil Sour

SWEET
Bell
Court Royal
Dunkerton's Late
Honeystring
Improved Woodbine
Le Bret
Morgan Sweet
Red Worthy
Slack-ma-Girdle
Sweet Alford
Sweet Coppin
Sweet Pethyre

Taylor's Sweet
Woodbine

BITTERSHARP
Cap of Liberty
Kingston Black
Lambrook Pippin
Lorna Doone
Porter's Perfection
Sharpshooter
Stembridge Clusters
Stoke Red
Yellow Redstreak

DUAL PURPOSE
Buttery Door
Congresbury Beauty
Court de Wick
Hoary Morning
King's Favourite
Long Tom
Pig's Snout
Poor Man's Profit
Royal Somerset
Sheep's Nose
Shoreditch White
Sops in Wine
Stubbard
Ten Commandments
Tom Putt
Wear and Tear

KEY TO IDENTIFICATION

BITTERSWEET VARIETIES

Shape	Strongly flushed predominantly diffuse	Lightly flushed usually striped	Flush absent or slight
Elongated conical	Tremletts Bitter Stable Jersey	Improved Dove Dove	Broad Leaf Jersey Michelin
Flattened conical	Ashton Brown Jersey Burrow Hill Jersey Dabinett Early Red Jersey Norton Bitters Pennard Bitter Somerset Redstreak	Coat Jersey Stembridge Jersey Pennard Bitter Vilberie	Bulmers Norman Cadbury Vilberie
Conical	Ashton Bitter Ashton Brown Jersey Chisel Jersey Early Red Jersey Ellis Bitter Harry Masters' Jersey Red Jersey Royal Jersey Stable Jersey Tommy Rodford Tremletts Bitter	Coat Jersey Dove Improved Dove Major Norton Bitters Stembridge Jersey White Close Pippin Yarlington Mill	Bulmers Norman Brown Snout Michelin White Jersey
Cylindrical	Ashton Brown Jersey Churchill Fillbarrel Norton Bitters	Camelot Hangdown	Camelot Hangdown Imp. Hangdown Silver Cup

SHARP AND DUAL PURPOSE VARIETIES

Shape	Strongly flushed predominantly diffuse	Lightly flushed usually striped	Flush absent or slight
Elongated conical	Wear and Tear	Pig's Snout Sheep's Nose	Cider Lady's Finger Stubbard
Flattened conical	Langworthy Red Tom Putt Ten Commandments	Hoary Morning King's Favourite Tom Putt	Fair Maid Taunton Gin Shoreditch Yeovil Sour
Conical	Backwell Red Crimson King Profit	Profit Sheep's Nose	Neverblight Sheep's Nose Somerset
Cylindrical	Backwell Red Brown's Apple Congresbury Beauty Imp. Kingston Black Royal Somerset Sops in Wine	Imp. Lambrook Pip. Long Tom	Court de Wick Gin Stubbard
Oblate	Brown's Apple Crimson King Imp. Kingston Black Ten Commandments Vallis Apple	Hoary Morning	Buttery Door Fair Maid Taunton
Round	Langworthy Sops in Wine	Imp. Lambrook Pippin	Court de Wick

BITTERSHARP VARIETIES

Shape	Strongly flushed, predominantly diffuse	Lightly flushed usually striped	Flush absent or slight
Flattened conical	Kingston Black Porter's Perfection	Lorna Doone Yellow Redstreak	Lorna Doone
Conical	Cap of Liberty Porter's Perfection	Stembridge Clusters	
Cylindrical	Cap of Liberty Kingston Black	Sharpshooter Stembridge Clusters	
Oblate	Lambrook Pippin	Lambrook Pippin	
Round	Stoke Red Sharpshooter	Sharpshooter	

PURE SWEET VARIETIES

Shape	Strongly flushed predominantly diffuse	Lightly flushed usually striped	Flush absent or slight
Elongated conical		Bell	
Flattened	Improved Woodbine		Honeystring Sweet Alford
Conical	Dunkertons Late Red Worthy	Le Bret Taylor's Sweet	Morgan Sweet Sweet Coppin Sweet Pethyre
Cylindrical	Dunkertons Late	Le Bret Taylor's Sweet	Sweet Coppin Sweet Pethyre
Oblate	Court Royal Improved Woodbine Slack-ma-Girdle	Slack-ma-Girdle Woodbine	
Round	Court Royal		

SYNONYMS

Batchelor's Glory:	Hoary Morning
Bear and Tear:	Wear and Tear
Bell;	Sheep's Nose
Bewley Down Pippin:	Crimson King
Bitter Jersey:	Chisel Jersey
Black Dabinett:	Tommy Rodford
Black Taunton:	Kingston Black
Black Vallis:	Vallis Apple
Bloody Soldier:	Cap of Liberty
Broadleaves:	Broad Leaf Jersey
Brown Jersey:	Ashton Brown Jersey
Buttery Dough:	Buttery Door
Clusters:	Porter's Perfection
Coalbrook:	Tom Putt
Dainty Apple:	Hoary Morning
Dry Close:	White Close Pippin
Dunkerton's Sweet:	Dunkerton's Late
Fry's Pippin:	Court de Wick
Gatcombe:	Gin
Golden Drop:	Court de Wick
Greasy Butcher:	Fair Maid of Taunton
Hang-me-Down:	Hangdown
Hangydown:	Hangdown
Hoary Jack:	Hoary Morning
Horners:	Hangdown
Improved Horners:	Improved Hangdown
Improved Pound:	Court Royal
Jacksons:	Crimson King
Jersey Chisel:	Chisel Jersey
John Toucher's:	Crimson King
Lambrook Seedling:	Hoary Morning
Laurel Grange:	Red Jersey
Loral Drang:	Red Jersey
Loyal Drain:	Red Jersey
Marrowbone:	Tom Putt
Masters' Jersey:	Harry Masters' Jersey
Meare Bitter:	Pennard Bitter
Moonlight:	Fair Maid of Taunton
Moonshines:	Fair Maid of Taunton
Nerton Bitter:	Norton Bitters

Neverblight:	Stoke Red
Osier:	Improved Hangdown
Pennard Dove:	Dove
Perfection (Sam Duck's):	Stembridge Clusters
Ploughman:	Tom Putt
Pocket Apple:	Hangdown
Pople's Gutter Apple:	Congresbury Beauty
Porter's Sheep's Nose:	Stembridge Clusters
Port Wine:	Early Red Jersey
	Harry Masters' Jersey
	Improved Kingston Black
Pound Apple:	Court Royal
Pounset:	Cadbury
Profit Apple:	Poor Man's Profit
Rank Shooter:	Sharpshooter
Redskins:	Vallis Apple
Red Soldiers:	Cap of Liberty
Red Vallis:	Vallis Apple
Rice's Jersey:	Woodbine
Rodford:	Tommy Rodford
Royal Jersey II:	Early Red Jersey
Royal Wildling:	Cadbury
Runaway:	Woodbine
Sapson:	Sops in Wine
Sapsovin:	Sops in Wine
Sheep's Nose:	Pig's Snout
Sidestalk Jersey:	Chisel Jersey
Slack-ma-Girl:	Slack-ma-Girdle
Sour Cadbury:	Neverblight
	Yeovil Sour
Sour Natural:	Langworthy
Stibbert:	Stubbard
Stoke Redstripe:	Stoke Red
Sweet Blenheim:	Court Royal
Sweet Sheep's Nose:	Bell
Taylor's Seedling:	Taylor's Sweet
Twistbody Jersey:	Coat Jersey
White Wine:	Somerset
Wyatt's Seedling/Sweet:	Langworthy

STANDARD TREES OF GOOD VINTAGE QUALITY
from MAFF Bulletin No. 104, Cider Apple Production, 1947
by B.T.P. Barker

Full Bittersharp

Cap of Liberty — Sugar content high; full bodied; fermentation slow. Of high quality for blending.

Medium Bittersharp

Kingston Black — Sugar content very high in good years; body full; fermentation slow. Of outstanding merit; ranks now as the best English vintage variety.

Lambrook Pippin — Sugar content and body very fair; fermentation moderate. Yields a nice, light, bottling cider. A very useful late variety.

Neverblight — Sugar content average; fermentation inclined to be rapid; cider of medium quality. The special merit of this variety is its resistance to pests and diseases, as its name implies.

Porter's Perfection — Sugar content very fair; body good; fermentation slow. Yields a superior cider in suitable seasons.

Stoke Red — Sugar content above average; good body; fermentation slow generally. This variety is distinguished by high vintage and orchard qualities.

Medium Sharp

Backwell Red — Sugar content moderate; body very fair; fermentation moderate to slow. For an early variety yields a good cider.

Crimson King — Sugar content rather low generally; body light; fermentation rather rapid. Yields a fair cider for blending.

Gin — Sugar content rather above average; fermentation slow to medium; vintage quality good. Its late blossoming habit, good and consistent cropping quality and its cider characters merit wider trial of this variety.

Improved Kingston Black — Sugar content average; fermentation rather rapid. Its name is a misnomer in respect of its vintage quality, although the variety crops better and is less susceptible to scab and canker than the Kingston Black proper.

Langworthy — Sugar content average; body variable, but very fair generally; fermentation moderate to slow. A very useful variety.

Yeovil Sour — Sugar content average; fermentation medium. Yields a medium-brisk cider, of attractive character in favourable seasons.

Sweet

Court Royal — Sugar content good; fermentation rapid. Gives a high yield of somewhat coarse type of cider.

Morgan Sweet — Sugar content low; fermentation rapid. High yield of juice. Cider usually of moderate and rather coarse character. A variety entitled to consideration for its orchard value, earliness, and high juice yield rather than for its vintage quality.

Slack-ma-Girdle — Sugar content very fair; fermentation moderate. Very fair vintage value, but usually of rather coarser flavour than Sweet Alford.

Woodbine — Sugar content average; fermentation slow to medium; of useful quality for blending.

Mild Bittersweet

Ashton Brown Jersey — Sugar content above average; fermentation slow to medium and readily controllable; vintage quality good. These features in conjunction with its satisfactory orchard characters and heavy cropping habit make this Long Ashton variety a valuable addition to the higher grades of English cider apples.

Dove — Sugar a little below average generally; fermentation slow; cider quality very fair. Profitable for the grower and useful to the cider-maker.

Hangdown — Sugar content good; fermentation moderate; yields a cider of good quality for blending.

Thomas Hunt — Sugar content above average; fermentation rather rapid; yields a useful cider for blending.

Tremlett's Bitter. — Sugar content rather low; fermentation rather slow. Cider of very fair quality.

White Jersey — Sugar content good for an early variety; fermentation slow to moderate; yields an attractive cider for blending.

Medium Bittersweet

Broadleaf Jersey — Sugar content moderate; fermentation usually rather rapid; cider quality indifferent to moderate. A variety grown rather extensively in some parts of Somerset years ago, which might well be superseded by better varieties of its class.

Cadbury — Sugar content high; fermentation slow to medium. In favourable seasons yields a cider of very high quality and is generally well above average.

Dabinett — Sugar content fair; fermentation moderate. Quality of cider generally well above average. A most valuable variety for the orchard and cider factory.

Harry Masters' Jersey — Sugar content above average; fermentation medium to slow. A bittersweet cider of merit.

Port Wine — Sugar content above average; fermentation rather irregular. Makes a rich cider. Regarded as one of the best all round sorts by those who grow it.

Red Jersey — Sugar content average; fermentation slow. Cider of good medium bittersweet type.

Silver Cup — Sugar content high; fermentation slow to medium. Gives a full-bodied rich cider of attractive flavour and aroma. A little-known variety of much promise, if cropping can be improved.

White Close Pippin — Sugar content above average; fermentation inclined to be slow. Cider of useful body, flavour and aroma.

Yarlington Mill — Sugar content often above average; fermentation slow to medium. Cider of good body, aroma and flavour usually. A superior all-round variety.

Full Bittersweet

Chisel Jersey — Sugar content good; fermentation slow to medium. Yields a cider of marked astringency, usually of full body and good flavour and aroma.

Major — Sugar content good for so early a variety; fermentation rather slow; its cider is among the best of the bittersweets of its season.

Royal Jersey — Sugar content high; fermentation slow to moderate. Cider of full body, bitter but rich flavour, and good aroma.

USEFUL NAMES AND ADDRESSES

NURSERY TREES

SUPPLIERS OF DESSERT AND CULINARY VARIETIES

Mark Wallis, Scotts Nursery, Merriott, Somerset TA16 5PL
  01460 72306

Highfield Nurseries, Whitminster, Gloucestershire, GL2 7PL
  01452 740266

AND ALSO CIDERS

Frank P Matthews, Berrington Court, Tenbury Wells, Worcs
  WR15 8TH   01584 810 214

SPECIALIST SUPPLIER OF WEST COUNTRY VARIETIES AND CIDER APPLES

Kevin Croucher, Thornhayes Nursery, Dulford, Cullompton, Devon
  EX15 2DF   01884 266746

SUPPLIERS OF CIDER APPLE VARIETIES ONLY

Matthew Clark, Kilver Street, Shepton Mallet, BA4 5ND
  01749 334000

Bulmers Orcharding, Plough Lane, Hereford, HR4 0LE
  01432 345285

John Dennis, 12 Tallowood, Shepton Mallet, BA4 5QM
  01749 343368

COLLECTIONS

Matthew Clark PLC, Kilver Street, Shepton Mallet, Somerset,
  BA4 5ND   01749 334000

Thatchers Cider Company, Myrtle Farm, Sandford, N.Somerset
  BS19 5RA   01934 822862

Bulmers Cider Company, Plough Lane, Hereford, HR4 0LE
  01432 352000

National Fruit Collection, Brogdale Horticultural Trust, Brogdale
  Road, Faversham, Kent, ME13 8XZ 01795 535 286

ORGANISATIONS

National Association of Cider Makers;
  Orcharding advice, Liz Copas, IACR Long Ashton, BS41 9AF
  Head Office, Food & Drink House, 6 Catherine Street, London
  WC2B 5JJ   02078 360580

Common Ground, 45 Shelton Street, London WC2H 9HJ
  02073 793109
  Initiated Apple Day 21st October, information on conservation and
  orchards.

Royal Horticultural Society, 80 Vincent Square, London SW1P 2PE
  0207 8344333

Somerset Countryside Services Group, County Hall, Taunton
  TA1 4DY   01823 355420. Restoration, planting and
  maintenance grants.

SOMERSET CIDER MAKERS

Ashwood Cider, Shipham Hill, Cheddar.

Ben Crossman, Mayfield Farm, Hewish, Weston-super-Mare.

Coombes Cider, Japonica Farm, Mark, Highbridge. 01278 641265

Dobunni Fruit Farm, Brean Road, Lympsham. 01278 751593

Hecks, Middle Street, Leigh, Street. 01458 442367

Matthew Clark PLC, Kilver Street, Shepton Mallet. 01749 334000

Parsons Choice, Parsons Farm, West Lyng, Taunton. 01823 490978

Perry's Cider Mills, Dowlish Wake, Ilminster. 01460 52681

Richards, Land Farm, Congresbury.

Rich's Farmhouse Cider, Watchfield, Nr Highbridge. 01278 783651

Sheppey's Cider, Three Bridges, Bradford-on-Tone, Taunton.
  01823 461233

Somerset Cider Brandy Company and Burrow Hill Cider, Kingsbury
  Episcopi, Martock. 01460 240782

Thatchers Cider Company, Myrtle Farm, Sandford, N.Somerset.
  01934 822862

West Croft Cider, Brent Knoll, Highbridge. 01278 760762

Wilkins, Land's End Farm, Mudgley, Wedmore. 01934 712385

FURTHER READING

Barker, B.T.P., Vintage Characters of Cider Apples, from MAFF Bulletin No 104, Cider Apple Production, 1947

Barron, A.F., *British Apples* (Macmillan), 1884

Billingsley, J., *Agricultural Survey of Somerset*, 1798

Chittenden, F.J., *Apples and Pears, varieties and cultivation in 1934*, Report of RHS Conference 1934, (Royal Horticultural Society), 1935

Crowden, James, *Bottling it up* (Nonesuch, University of Bristol), 2000

Evelyn, John, *Pomona* (John Martyn and James Allestry), 1670

Foot, Mark, *Cider's Story, Rough and Smooth*, 1999

Hogg, Robert, *The Apple and Pear as Vintage Fruits* (Jakeman and Carver), 1886

Hogg, Robert, *The Fruit Manual* (Cottage Gardener Office), 1860

Knight, T.A., *Pomona Herefordensis* (Agricultural Society of Hereford), 1811

Langley, Batty, *Pomona* (G. Strahan), 1729

Legg, Philippa, *So merry let us be. . . The living tradition of Somerset cider* (Somerset County Council), 1986

Lindley, George, *A guide to the orchard and kitchen garden* (Longman), 1831

Lloyd, F.J., *Observations and Experiments in cider-making*, Report of the Bath and West and Southern Counties Society, 1893-1902

Long Ashton Research Station, Annual Reports, 1903-37

Marsh R.W., *The National Fruit and Cider Institute: 1903-1983, Annual Report*, Long Ashton Research Station, 1983

Mid-Somerset Agricultural Society, *Proceedings of the 1st Cider Conference*, 1903, Long Ashton Research Station

Morgan, Joan and Richards, Alison, *The Book of Apples* In association with Brogdale Trust (Ebury Press), 1993

National Association of Cider Makers, *Cider*, 1980

Phillips, Henry, *Pomona Britannicum* (T. and J. Allman), 1822

Roach, F.A., *Apple Production in England – Its History from Roman Times to the Present Day*, Annual Report, Long Ashton Research Station, 1979

Roe, Capt.R.G.B., *The Flora of Somerset*, Somerset Archaeological and Natural History Society, 1981

Royal Horticultural Society, *Apples and Pears, Varieties and Cultivation in 1934*

Scott, J., *Scott's Orchardist* (Pollett), 1873

Smith, M.W.G., *National Apple Register of the United Kingdom* (MAFF), 1971

Somerset Farm Institute, Cannington, Advisory Report, 1935

Taylor, H.V., *The Apples of England* (Crosby Lockwood and Son Ltd), 1936

Wallace, T. and Marsh, R.W., *Science and Fruit* (University of Bristol), 1953

Williams R.R., *Cider and Juice Apples: Growing and Processing* (University of Bristol), 1987

Williams R.R. and Child R.D., *Cider apples and their characters*, Annual Report, 1962-65

ACKNOWLEDGEMENTS

The author would like to thank all those who helped with the identification of apples in old orchards around the county, including; Geoff Rowson, Les Davies and Tony Calder formerly of Showerings and together a mine of information; Paul Rendell who brought me many 'new' apples; Bill Dunkerton of Baltonsborough; and Jo King and Jim Dowling for the forays around Pilton for Gabriel's Millennium Orchard. Also many thanks to Peter Aikens, Chief Executive of Matthew Clark PLC, for allowing me to roam his private cider apple collection; and to my colleagues at the National Fruit Collection at Brogdale, Kent, for all their help and detective work.

Thanks to Long Ashton Research Station for the archive photographs of the early days, and recognition to those unknown workers who made all those detailed records of fruit and cider which I have been able to bring together for this book.

Special thanks to Ray Williams, formerly Cider Pomologist at Long Ashton Research Station, my senior for many years, who inspired my enthusiasm in orcharding and taught me much about cider apples.

And credit to my husband, Ronnie, for putting up with a house full of cider apples every autumn.